ACCIDENT INVESTIGATION TECHNIQUES

• Basic Theories

• Analytical Methods

• Applications

Jeffrey S. Oakley, Ph.D., CSP
University of Houston–Clear Lake

AMERICAN SOCIETY OF SAFETY ENGINEERS
DES PLAINES, ILLINOIS USA

Accident Investigation Techniques
©2003 by the American Society of Safety Engineers

Library of Congress Cataloging-in-Publication Data

Oakley, Jeffrey S.
    Accident investigation techniques : basic theories, analytical methods, and applications / Jeffrey S. Oakley.
      p. cm.
    Includes bibliographical references and index.
    ISBN 1-885581-47-5 (alk. paper)
      1. Industrial accidents—Investigation. 2. Accident investigation.
    I. American Society of Safety Engineers. II. Title.

HD7262.25.O35 2003
363.1'065—dc22

2003060502

Project Editor: Charles T. Coffin, ASSE
Managing Editor: Michael Burditt, ASSE
Copyediting, Text Design and Composition: Sue Knopf, Graffolio
Cover Design: Michael Burditt, ASSE

Printed in the United States

10 9 8 7 6 5 4 3 2 1

Contents

Computerized Techniques
Graphical Programs
Analytical Programs

*This book is dedicated
to my wife and son.*

Acknowledgments

I gratefully acknowledge all of the researchers of accident investigation and causation from whom I have drawn inspiration. I recognize H. W. Heinrich, Ludwig Benner, Ted Ferry, Leon Robertson, Dan Peterson, Frank Bird, William Haddon, William Johnson, Trevor Kletz, and Joe Stephenson for paving a path toward making accident investigation an important part of the safety process. I also recognize the Department of Energy, Department of Defense, Occupational Safety and Health Administration, and the Chemical Safety Board for their dedication to accident investigation.

I thank Daniel Herrera for his research help and for providing me with what seemed like an endless stream of articles and books about accident investigation. To my technical book reviewers, Greg Smith and Jeff Daggs, thanks for keeping me on track. I also thank Chuck Coffin of ASSE and Susan Knopf for editing the book.

I also acknowledge Battelle Memorial Institute and the Department of Energy for giving me the experience to write this book—and to Dale Moul and Steve Kirchoff of Battelle and Dennis Vernon of the Department of Energy, thanks for all of your help over the years.

Preface

All companies at some point must conduct accident investigations, and each company must decide how thoroughly to investigate and how much time and attention should be paid to the investigations. Many companies perform excellent accident investigations, but then fail to take corrective actions to fix the problems. Other companies do the opposite—they fail to determine the underlying causes of the accident, but just try to produce a "quick fix." Many techniques can be used to help companies and safety professionals to analyze accidents and feel assured that causes have been determined and corrective actions will prevent recurrence. This book presents techniques that can be applied to small, medium, and even large-scale accident investigations. By using these analytical techniques, you can prevent accidents at your workplace.

The book is divided into four parts and includes an Appendix of worksheets and charts. You may remove or copy these forms for your own use.

Part I is an introduction to the accident sequence. This part focuses on the theory of accidents, the accident sequence (sequence of events that happen before and during an accident), and the analytical approach to accidents. Research in the area of accidents, accident sequence, accident theory, root cause, and analytical approaches is discussed.

Part II describes the organization of accident investigations: starting the investigation, gaining knowledge about the accident, collecting evidence and data, and using appropriate investigative techniques. It includes instructions for gathering information, interviewing, documenting, preserving evidence, retrieving data, and analytically processing this information to determine exactly what happened.

Part III provides thorough explanations of analytical techniques that are useful in investigating accidents. Numerous examples and worksheets are included, and the benefits, weaknesses, and appropriateness of each technique are discussed. Four chapters of Part III are devoted to specific techniques, and a fifth covers other specialized and computerized techniques.

Part IV is devoted to accident prevention. After you use analytical techniques to determine what happened, the next step is to use that information to prevent future accidents. This part covers accident documentation and follow-up activities, and tells how to develop recommendations and corrective actions.

Jeffrey S. Oakley

Part I

INTRODUCTION TO THE ACCIDENT SEQUENCE

Accidents do not just happen—they are caused, and the key to accident investigation is to find the causes. The first step in finding the cause of an accident is to examine the sequence of events that led up to it. Discovering this sequence is the goal of many of the analytical techniques discussed later in the book. This part of the book includes many theories that have been developed to determine how accidents occur. Many have been and continue to be used, and many others have been disproven. This book will mention many theories, but will focus on those that are based on the accident sequence.

The objective of this book is to present an analytical approach to accident investigations—gathering evidence, using analytical techniques and the analytical process to determine the accident sequence, and using this information to discover the causes and to recommend changes to prevent future accidents.

Objectives for Part I:

- Understand that accidents have a sequence of events and be able to determine this sequence.

- Be familiar with several accident causation theories and know how each applies to the accident sequence.
- Be aware that most accidents have multiple causes.
- Be able to break down accidents and use an analytical approach to investigate them.

CHAPTER 1

An Accident Happens:
What Do You Do?
How Long Do You Do It?

These two questions are major issues of accident investigation that must be addressed and answered. Answering the first is simple: provide emergency response, protect the employees involved from further harm, and try to determine what happened so that measures can be taken to prevent its happening again. Answering the second question is more difficult. Some companies commit a specific amount of time to an accident investigation—a day, two weeks, or a month, for example—depending on the severity of the accident. In a perfect world, there is no time limit—an accident investigator investigates an accident until he or she is reasonably certain of what happened and why. This book answers the first question—it tells you what to do—and it provides ways to decrease the amount of time it takes to do it.

Accident investigations are a dreadful part of a safety professional's job. Accident outcomes may include injuries, fatalities, and property or equipment damage. It is sometimes difficult to "get over" the outcome of an accident, especially if there is a fatality or an employee is hospitalized because of it. However, accident investigations are a necessary and critical part of the occupational safety process. A thorough accident investigation can be of great benefit to your organization, not only by preventing the same type of accident from happening again, but also by finding systemic problems that could cause more severe accidents in the future. The main purpose of an accident investigation is to find the causes (what happened) and fix the problems to prevent the accident from recurring. "Accidents do not just happen, but are caused" (Marshall 2000, 29).

Definition of Terms

Accident

There are many definitions for "accident." Most books agree that an accident is an undesired event that causes injury or property damage (Bird and Germain 1985). Many companies use the term "incident" rather than "accident" because "accident" implies human error, while, according to the National Safety Council, "an incident is an unintentional event that may cause personal harm or other damage" (National Safety Council 2001, viii). The definition of "accident" that best captures the analytical approach to accident investigation is "That occurrence in a sequence of events that produces unintended injury, death, or property damage" (National Safety Council 2001, viii). These definitions and others are listed in Exhibit 1.1.

Near Miss

The difference between an accident and a near miss is usually luck or chance. A near miss is an occurrence in a sequence of events that had the *potential* to produce injury, death, or property damage but did not. Near misses can and should be investigated the same way accidents are.

Accident Investigation

An accident investigation is a structured process that attempts to uncover the sequence of events that produced or had the potential to produce injury, death, or property damage so that causal factors can be determined and corrective actions can be taken. Any occurrence that has a sequence of events can be investigated by analytical techniques—first-aid cases, OSHA-recordable injuries or illnesses, fatalities, property damage, or near misses. The steps in an accident investigation are analyzing the facts, developing an accident sequence, finding the causes, and recommending corrective action.

The next definitions have to do with the accident itself. Safety professionals use various terms for the basic terminology of the profession (Sorrell 1998); this book simplifies the definitions.

Causal Factors

The causes of the accident are called the *causal factors*. A causal factor is an event or circumstance that produced an accident. Other books may use the the term "root cause" to mean something similar. Causal factors can be at the basic (worker or equipment) level, the intermediate (supervisory) level, and the upper management level. The causal factors of an accident answer the question "What happened?" After causal factors are determined through an analytical process, *corrective actions* are developed to prevent similar types of accidents.

Corrective Actions

Corrective actions are the actions taken to prevent recurrence of the accident. Causal factors link to corrective actions to address all levels of causes and accountability (see Exhibit 1.1, Definitions).

Exhibit 1.1

DEFINITIONS

Accident—The occurrence in a sequence of events that produces unintended injury, death, or property damage.

Incident—An unintentional event that may cause personal harm or other damage.

Near Miss—An occurrence in a sequence of events that had the potential to produce injury, death, or property damage but did not.

Accident Investigation—A structured process of uncovering the sequence of events that produced or had the potential to produce injury, death, or property damage to determine the causal factors and corrective actions.

Causal Factors—Events and circumstances that produced the accident. Causal factors incorporate "root causes," "basic causes," "immediate causes," lower level causes, upper level causes, and management causes. When discovering causal factors, it is important to analyze all causes at all levels.

Corrective Actions—The actions taken to prevent recurrence of the accident. Corrective actions are the "fixes" to prevent future accidents. These fixes should be performed at the appropriate level

Goals of Accident Investigation

Determine the Accident Sequence without Placing Blame

An accident investigation determines the accident sequence and finds the causal factors of an accident. Its purpose is not to find fault or assign blame.

How do you keep from finding fault when an individual disregards a major safety policy? The answer is to be fair and consistent with your policy. If there is no accountability for violating a safety policy or disregarding the safety program, then the safety program will eventually fail. The main issue is to find out why the individual violated the safety policy. The accident investigator must determine why the safety program allowed the individual to disregard the rule and why supervisors did not enforce the rule. While these types of situations are rare, it is imperative for companies to correct problems with their safety programs to keep accidents from happening (Sorrell 1998).

Recommend Corrective Actions

Accident investigations determine corrective actions so that future accidents are prevented and the overall safety program is improved.

Update the Overall Safety Program

By identifying hazards from the worker level up to the management systems level, the safety program can be updated and improved.

Accident Reporting

Thorough Reporting Is Necessary

Accidents cannot be investigated if they are not properly reported. All accidents, including fatalities, injuries, and property damage, as well as potential accidents (near misses), should be reported. Formal company policy and employee training must spell out how to properly and consistently report accidents, near misses, and property damage (Vincoli 1994). Individuals must have no fear of repercussions for informing the company or the safety department of an accident or near miss. If people fear punishment or repercussion (accusation of fault or blame) for accidents, they are less likely to report them (Speir 1998). It is crucial to a company's safety program and to the prevention of future accidents that all accidents and near misses be reported so that all of the problems in the safety program can be found.

Incentive Programs Must Reward Reporting

Incentive programs have been developed to reward safe behaviors. Unfortunately, many of them do not actually reward safe behavior but instead inhibit the reporting of accidents and near misses because employees fear losing their incentives. Such incentives do not improve safety programs. Reporting accidents and near misses, finding causal factors, and determining corrective actions, however, will improve them. Reporting accidents and near misses should be rewarded, and incentive programs should be designed to reward the reporting of all accidents and near misses.

Why Do We Need Accident Investigations?

To Avoid Spending Money on Accidents in the Future

Accidents are a major expense for companies. According to the 2003 edition of *Injury Facts,* in 2002 the total cost of unintentional injuries at work was $146.6 billion dollars (National Safety Council 2003). This monetary figure does not reflect the cost of human pain and suffering as a result of accidents. In 2002, 4,900 fatal occupational injuries occurred and 3.7 million injuries were reported (National Safety Council 2003).

Bird and Germain compare the costs of an accident to an iceberg—like an iceberg, most of the costs of an accident are not obvious and are not seen. For every dollar of medical and insurance costs an injury or illness incurs, the uninsured costs are $5 to $50 and miscellaneous costs are $1 to $3. The uninsured costs include damage to equipment, tools, and products; production delays; and legal expenses. The miscellaneous costs include accident investigation expenses, hiring replacement workers, and loss of business (Bird and Germain 1985).

As expensive as an accident may be, the resulting investigation can ultimately save money by helping to prevent future accidents and update safety programs. Future savings will be found in identifying systemic problems in the safety program and correcting them. Near misses are excellent opportunities to prevent costly accidents and identify and deal with systemic problems in the safety program.

Accident costs come directly from a company's bottom line. While saving money is a great motivator for improving safety procedures, a bigger motivator is avoiding the pain and suffering accidents produce. The field of occupational safety is very dynamic, with theories and concepts that change over time. However, most people would agree that "the ultimate goal of all efforts in safety engineering should be to reduce accidents and harmful exposures" (Marshall 2000, 6).

To Prevent Future Accidents

An accident investigation cannot do anything for the person already injured, the machine already damaged, or the product already destroyed. Its value is in preventing future accidents. Although investigations are performed reactively, they allow companies to be proactive in improving their safety programs.

To Comply with the Law and
Determine the Total Cost of an Accident

Accident investigations must also be performed to complete workers' compensation claims, to comply with legal requirements and Occupational Safety and Health Administration (OSHA) regulations, and to determine the total costs of accidents.

Decisions to Be Made
Before an Investigation Begins

Determine the Level of Investigation

Companies define levels of accidents and levels of accident investigations to help answer questions about how an investigation will be conducted—such as how much detail the investigation should uncover and how long the investigation should take. In general, the more serious an accident is, the more detailed the investigation will be and the longer it will take. The philosophy of this book is that whether an accident is minor or catastrophic, the investigation process still follows the same steps—develop the accident sequence, analyze it, determine causal factors, and recommend corrective actions. The levels of accidents and types of accident investigations are listed in Exhibit 1.2.

Decide Who Will Investigate

Once the accident level and the depth of investigation are determined, your company must decide whether to use an individual or a team to do the investigation. Many people from throughout your organization may be able to perform adequate accident investigations. The key is to choose the person (or persons) who is in the best position to discover what really happened and determine how to

Exhibit 1.2

CATEGORIZATION OF ACCIDENTS	
LEVELS OF ACCIDENTS	**TYPES OF ACCIDENT INVESTIGATIONS**
1. Near miss	Near misses can range from potentially minor to potentially catastrophic accidents. At the least, document the near miss on a form, determine its causes, and recommend corrective actions.
2. Minor injury or first-aid case	Investigate, interview injured employee, determine causes, and recommend corrective actions. Document on a form.
3. Major injury or recordable injury	Investigate, interview the injured employee and witnesses, use analytical techniques, determine causes, and recommend corrective actions. Write a short report.
4. Catastrophic injury (fatality, many injured, or major property damage)	Team investigation. Interview injured, eyewitnesses, and other employees; use analytical techniques; determine causes; and recommend corrective actions. Write a full report explaining the analytical techniques used.

prevent it from happening again. Foremen and supervisors are excellent choices if they are able to look beyond their departments to systemic causes—problems with the overall system of safety management. They usually understand the workers' jobs and the roles supervisors should play. Safety professionals can do investigations, but usually they do not fully understand all of the workers' job functions, so they must spend time learning job duties and sequences. A more useful role for safety professionals is providing assistance to accident investigators, since safety professionals are trained to uncover and analyze systemic causes and management system causes.

The Team Approach

For large or complex accidents, the team approach to accident investigation seems logical because more information must be analyzed than with less serious accidents. The usual team approach is to appoint a team leader who oversees and manages the investigation. The number of individuals on the team will vary depending on the accident's complexity. Normally, subject matter experts will be used to lend expertise about the complex issues that will be uncovered in the accident investigation.

In order for a team investigation to work effectively, the team leader must assign each subject matter expert to work in his or her area of expertise. Having the subject matter experts work separately on the overall investigation rather than concentrating on their own areas is a waste of time. Each subject matter expert should have a separate area to focus on, such as a technical or engineering issue, training, management systems, supervision, emergency response, etc. The team leader coordinates all of the efforts and ensures that all of the subject matter experts are working toward a common goal— finding out what happened and how to prevent it.

Decide How Much Time Will Be Allotted to the Investigation

Deciding how much time the investigators will be given to perform the investigation and document the findings is a difficult decision. Many companies allot a set amount of time based on the level of the accident and the type of investigation to be performed. Ideally, the company should allow enough time to find out what happened and determine how to prevent it from recurring. In most cases, a first-aid case or an OSHA-recordable case will take a few days, while a major injury, fatality, or other complex accident may take anywhere from a couple of days to a month. Investigations of catastrophes with multiple fatalities and involving complex systems (plant explosions, plane crashes, etc.) usually take from a month to several years. The time needed to perform investigations at any level depends on the amount of data collected, the number of interviews, the number of people helping with the investigation, the analytical methods used, the complexity of the systems involved, and the length of the final report or form.

Determine Whether Additional Resources Will Be Needed

For the most part, this book discusses nonproprietary investigation techniques that do not require extra expenses. However, in many investigations, consultants (subject matter experts, medical doctors, lawyers) or special equipment (testing equipment, external testing, laboratory work, computer software) may be needed. Coordinating these resources will extend the time needed to perform an investigation.

Summary

The basic requirement for a successful accident investigation program is a formal accident-reporting policy with proper and consistent reporting of all accidents and near misses from employees who do not fear repercussions. In the past, most accident investigations began with the question "Who did it?" In a modern investigation, the accident investigator must concentrate on causal factors and corrective actions and not place blame. Accident investigations should be conducted by a qualified individual or team. The purpose of the investigation is to find the causal factors of the accident and determine the corrective actions to prevent recurrence of the accident as well as to find systemic causes and thus prevent other types of accidents in the future.

Accident investigations are a necessary part of the occupational safety process. Although proactive accident prevention and loss control strategies are the main purpose of a safety program, accidents will occur. The company and the accident investigator must learn from each accident and revise the safety program as needed.

REVIEW QUESTIONS

1. What are the goals of accident investigations?

2. Why is it important to conduct accident investigations?

3. What are the levels of accidents?

4. Accident investigations can point out what types of problems in the safety program?

5. Who should conduct an accident investigation?

CHAPTER 2

A Short History
of Accident Theory

There are many theories about why and how accidents occur, and understanding them is important. An accident investigator must understand how an accident occurs in order to properly analyze it, find its causes, and prevent future accidents. This book presents several accident theories. You will need to use all of them—and perhaps challenge them, too.

Accident theories are continually challenged and revised, and some of the theories discussed here contradict each other. Each accident investigator and company has a view about how accidents occur and which theories they prefer. This book emphasizes finding the sequence of events that occurred as an accident unfolded. It teaches the analytical techniques you can use to find accident causes as well as the multiple causation theory discussed in this chapter.

Most accident investigators and safety professionals have read about and used the domino theory, which will be discussed later in this chapter. H. W. Heinrich developed this theory, and many researchers after him, including Frank Bird and George Germain, have researched and updated it. While the domino theory can be useful, it seems to force investigators to follow a strict model. Since every accident and every investigation is different, a simpler theory that emphasizes the uniqueness of each accident is needed—one that helps the investigator to discover the unique sequence of events that led to an accident.

You may have watched television shows or movies about criminal investigators who seem to have special powers that allow them to discover how a crime took place. Unfortunately, most real-life accident investigators do not have these special powers and must learn analytical techniques to help them determine the sequence of actions and inactions that caused an accident. This book will help you to do that.

Accident Ratio Study

The Accident Ratio Study is not an accident causation theory per se, but it demonstrates an interesting fact: *A near miss or property damage event usually takes place before a major accident with injury.* This well-known study analyzed 1,753,498 accidents reported by 297 companies from 21 industrial groups. Three billion work-hours and 1,750,000 employees were represented. The study found that for every one serious or major injury, there were ten minor injuries, thirty property damage accidents, and six hundred incidents with no visible injury or damage (near misses) (Bird and O'Shell 1969). This accident ratio is shown in Exhibit 2.1. "The 1-10-30-600 relationships in the ratio indicate quite clearly how foolish it is to direct our major effort at the relatively few events resulting in serious or disabling injury when there are so many significant opportunities that provide a much larger basis for more effective control of total losses" (Bird and Germain 1985, 21).

What this study shows is that if all near misses and property damage events were investigated, major accidents might be avoided. Understanding this concept is important for people who perform accident investigations and people who are responsible for safety program enhancement. In most companies, there is some tolerance for

Exhibit 2.1

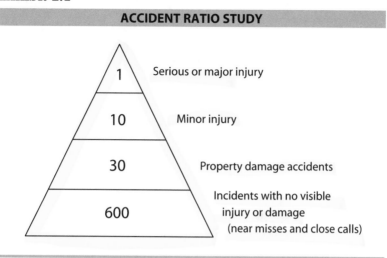

ACCIDENT RATIO STUDY

1	Serious or major injury
10	Minor injury
30	Property damage accidents
600	Incidents with no visible injury or damage (near misses and close calls)

Bird and Germain 1985, 21

near misses, a little less tolerance for minor injuries and property damage, and very little tolerance for major injuries. Major accidents are usually investigated thoroughly, and the problems discovered in the investigation are fixed so that the same kinds of accidents do not happen again. Minor accidents, however, do not receive the same attention, even though "fixing" them may prevent more serious accidents. Companies must encourage the reporting of near misses and property damage accidents, and they must support the thorough investigation of less-serious accidents in order to prevent more-serious ones.

Domino Theories

Heinrich's Domino Theory

G. W. Heinrich developed his *domino theory* of accident causation in 1931. It was the first domino theory of accidents (Heinrich 1931; Heinrich 1959), although more were developed later. Heinrich's version of the domino theory illustrates how an accident occurs by comparing

17

the events leading up to it to a set of dominos. The first domino (the first event) sets the stage and starts the accident sequence. When it falls, it pushes the next, and that pushes the next, until the last domino, which represents the accident or injury, is toppled. The domino theory is illustrated in Exhibit 2.2.

Heinrich identified five types of action that comprise an accident sequence: *ancestry and social environment, fault or person, unsafe act, unsafe condition,* and *injury.* "Heinrich showed that by removing one of the intervening dominos (a preventative action) the remaining ones would not fall, and there would be no injury" (Ferry 1981, 127). Heinrich's domino theory not only defined how accidents occur, but it also helped investigators to develop interventions and preventative measures to prevent accidents.

Bird and Germain's Domino Theory: The Loss Causation Model

Many safety professionals and accident investigators have refined and updated the domino theory since Heinrich's time. One of the more noteworthy updates is Bird and Germain's Loss Causation Model.

Exhibit 2.2

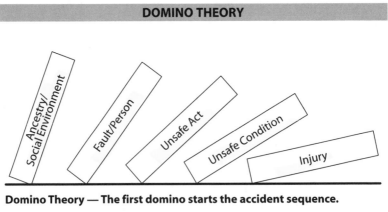

DOMINO THEORY

Domino Theory — The first domino starts the accident sequence.

Their domino theory also uses five dominos, but they have different titles—*lack of control, basic causes, immediate causes, the incident,* and *people/property/injury damage* (see Exhibit 2.3).

Each domino represents a step in an accident sequence:

- **Lack of control** includes failure to maintain compliance with adequate standards.

- The **basic causes** are the personal and job factors that started the accident sequence.

- The **immediate causes** are the substandard practices and conditions that existed at the time of the accident.

- The **incident** is what actually happened—What was struck? What was struck by something? What fell? What got caught? What made contact with something it shouldn't have? Who overexerted him- or herself?

- The **loss** is the injury or property damage that occurred (Bird and Germain 1985).

This domino model is widely used today in the safety profession, and the terms Bird and Germain use to explain their theory are also

Exhibit 2.3

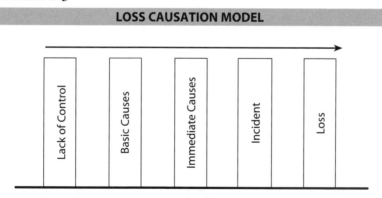

LOSS CAUSATION MODEL

Lack of Control | Basic Causes | Immediate Causes | Incident | Loss

Loss Causation Model — The accident sequence starts with lack of control and eventually leads to loss.

Bird and Germain 1985, 22

widely used, unfortunately sometimes out of context. The meanings of "basic causes" and "immediate causes" are subjects of debate. Many accident investigators use these terms without understanding what Bird and Germain intended them to mean. Understanding these two domino theories is extremely important to accident investigations and the theory of accident causation, and accident investigators must understand the terms and models associated with them. Many accident investigation training courses still study these models, and they are still actively used.

Unsafe Acts and Unsafe Conditions

The concept of "unsafe acts and unsafe conditions" was introduced in Heinrich's original domino theory of accident causation. Unsafe acts and unsafe conditions are the most important factors in determining the causes and corrective actions for accidents. These two concepts eventually evolved into a separate theory—to prevent accidents, you must remove the unsafe act or unsafe condition; to investigate accidents, you must determine the unsafe act or unsafe condition that caused the accident (Peterson 1978).

As part of researching their loss causation model, Bird and Germain developed lists of unsafe acts and conditions that can be considered "immediate causes" of accidents (their middle domino) (see Exhibit 2.4). You will notice that an unsafe act is usually something done by a person, while an unsafe condition is a failure of equipment or a problem in the work environment.

Many accident investigators and safety professionals in the 1970s and 1980s used Bird and Germain's lists to analyze accident causes. For each accident, they chose immediate causes that seemed to fit the accident from the "acts" and "conditions" lists, but they did little to investigate or analyze the accident. The loss causation model focuses on human error, and for many years human error and unsafe acts seemed to be the most common causal factors in accident reports.

Bird and Germain's lists represent a very simplistic view of accidents and do not include all of the causal factors of accidents. Researchers have calculated percentages indicating what proportion of all accidents each cause is responsible for, but the percentages are not included in this book because it is very possible that the accidents they were based on were not thoroughly investigated. Despite its drawbacks, however, the overall concept of the loss causation model is good— if we reduce the number of unsafe acts and conditions in our workplaces, we will have fewer accidents.

Exhibit 2.4

IMMEDIATE CAUSES OF ACCIDENTS IN THE LOSS CAUSATION MODEL	
UNSAFE ACTS	**UNSAFE CONDITIONS**
1. Operating equipment without authority	1. Inadequate guards and barriers
2. Failure to warn	2. Inadequate or improper protective equipment
3. Failure to secure	3. Defective tools, equipment, or materials
4. Operating at improper speed	4. Congestion or restricted action
5. Making safety devices inoperable	5. Inadequate warning system
6. Removing safety devices	6. Fire and explosion hazards
7. Using defective equipment	7. Poor housekeeping, disorder
8. Failing to use PPE properly	8. Noise exposure
9. Improper loading	9. Radiation exposure
10. Improper placement	10. Temperature extremes
11. Improper lifting	11. Inadequate or excess illumination
12. Improper position of task	12. Inadequate ventilation
13. Servicing equipment in operation	
14. Horseplay	
15. Under influence of alcohol and/or other drugs	

Bird and Germain 1985, 37

The Multiple Causation Theory

Accidents usually have more than one cause—they are rarely caused by one act or condition. The multiple causation theory expands the domino theory and the concept of unsafe acts and unsafe conditions: it proposes that each accident is usually the result of many acts, many conditions, and causes of many types—complex, simple, obvious, obscure, and systemic. The most important part of this theory is that investigators must use an analytical approach and analytical techniques to investigate an accident and find all of its causal factors. Most of the analytical techniques discussed in this book focus on finding multiple causes for accidents.

The multiple causation theory is consistent with the analytical techniques and theory of accident causation that government agencies use. *Management Oversight and Risk Tree (MORT) Root Cause Analysis,* developed by the Department of Energy, states:

> "When considering why an accident or incident occurred, more than one root cause must be considered. Very seldom will just one root cause create a condition that results in an accident. In most cases it requires a chain of root causes that reaches from top management to the lowest level of the work process. Correcting the specific root causes generally will only correct the bottom-level conditions. Correcting the systemic root causes is more likely to correct all of the root causes in a particular chain that reaches from management to the bottom work processes" (SSDC 1989, ii).

Discovering *all* of the causal factors of an accident is the key to fixing the problems that exist and preventing more accidents. If accident investigators analyze only "acts and conditions," they may miss many higher level issues. Dan Peterson discusses this principle in *Techniques of Safety Management:*

> "Today we know that behind every accident there lie many contributing factors, causes, and subcauses. The theory of

multiple causation states that these factors combine together in random fashion, causing accidents. If this is true, our investigation of accidents ought to identify as many of these factors as possible—certainly more than one act and/or condition" (Peterson 1978, 16).

A comparison of the multiple causation theory of accident investigation and the unsafe acts and unsafe conditions model is shown in Exhibit 2.5.

To find multiple causes, you must systematically and exhaustively ask questions and break down the accident into its parts so that you uncover all of the potential causes—from simple to complex—and thus help to prevent recurrence of the accident. The analytical techniques discussed in this book were developed to perform this type of analysis. If you do not find all of the causal factors during your investigation, more accidents may occur.

The Epidemiological Model

In the last fifty years, there has been much research on epidemiology—the study of how often diseases occur, how they are distributed, and how to control them. Scientists study the Epidemiological Triangle, which consists of the host (the person who gets a disease), the agent that causes the disease (virus, bacteria, etc.), and the vehicle or *vector* environment that carries the disease (mosquito, tick, water sources, etc.). In a similar way, investigators who use the epidemiological model of accident investigation identify a host (the person who was injured), the agent (what did the injuring), and the vector, vehicle, or environmental factor (what conveyed the agent) (Robertson 1998). These concepts are used to create a model of how the injury occurred.

Agents of injury are forms of energy—mechanical, thermal, chemical, electrical, or ionizing radiation. (In some cases, insufficient energy may be the agent.) The epidemiological model is excellent at determining the specific form of energy (agent) that caused the injury,

Exhibit 2.5

MULTIPLE CAUSATION THEORY
VS. UNSAFE ACTS/UNSAFE CONDITIONS

INVESTIGATIONS USING THE UNSAFE ACTS/UNSAFE CONDITIONS MODEL

Unsafe Act: An employee uses a defective ladder.

Unsafe Condition: The defective ladder.

Corrective Action: Take the defective ladder out of service. (While this is definitely a corrective action, other more systemic factors may need to be investigated.)

INVESTIGATIONS USING THE MULTIPLE CAUSATION THEORY

• Why did the employee use the defective ladder?

• Why was the ladder defective?

• Did any maintenance or inspections occur?

• Why did inspections not determine that the ladder was defective?

• Was the employee trained to recognize the hazards of defective equipment?

• Why was the employee not trained?

• Was a Job Safety Analysis performed on the job?

• Did the supervisor determine whether the job and equipment were safe?

• Is there a policy that describes how to take equipment out of service?

• Did the employee know that he or she had the right to stop the job if equipment was defective?

These questions could lead to finding multiple causes of the accident, including systemic ones that should be analyzed to prevent future accidents.

Adapted from Peterson 1978

illness, or damage. This agent can then be analyzed to find out how and why the agent produced the accident. An in-depth analysis not only will find causal factors, but also will help the investigator design preventive interventions and corrective actions that can be used to reduce the agent to a level that will not cause injury, illness, or damage.

Vehicles of injury include motor vehicles, equipment, guns and even the environment. Investigators must study vehicles of energy to determine how the agent was released. Was it expected or accidental? How did the release of energy cause the injury, illness, or damage?

The epidemiological model is probably too narrow in scope to be the only technique an investigator uses to study accidents. However, it works well in determining the local causes of the injury, illness, or damage and the immediate cause, and this model is still valid in the realm of disease control.

The Haddon Matrix Theory

One of the most useful accident investigation theories is the Haddon matrix, which is a way to graphically correlate the factors and phases of injury (Haddon 1972). It works with many dimensions of the accident sequence and the factors involved in the accident. In the Haddon matrix theory an accident has three distinct phases—*pre-injury, injury,* and *post-injury.*

In accident investigation terms, the pre-injury phase means the causes of the accident. For a person who fell from a ladder, the pre-injury phase could be climbing a wet ladder with oily boots, the injury phase would be the person's impact with ground, and the post-injury phase would be the concussion the person suffered. These phases of injury represent the entire accident sequence.

During each of the three phases, three factors influence the outcome of the event: human factors, equipment factors, and environmental factors. Investigators develop a matrix to categorize the factors that occurred during each phase. Once the matrix is filled in, it is possible to isolate and compare the interactions, develop causes, and recommend corrections (Metzgar 2003). The Haddon matrix theory is useful in determining how an accident occurred and finding causal factors. (See Exhibit 2.6.)

Exhibit 2.6

A HADDON MATRIX			
	FACTORS		
	Human	**Equipment**	**Environment**
Pre-Injury	Time pressure to perform the job (rushing job)	Oily boots	Rainy
Injury	Feet and hands slipping on ladder	Distance to ground (distance of fall)	Slippery ladder
Post-Injury	Concussion	Ladder fell over on top of employee	Emergency medical response late due to rain

(Left axis label: **PHASES**)

Other Accident Causation Theories

Technical or Engineering Approaches

Technical or engineering approaches to accident investigation are very specific and discover lower level causes and system failures. They are excellent for investigating system or equipment failure, but too narrow in scope for most other types of investigations.

Human Error or Human Factors Theories

Many types of human error methodologies have been created, but they are difficult to use without appearing to assess blame. However, some of the human factors theories that discuss interactions are very useful. These systems allow investigators to discover the interactions between humans, machines, and the environment. These types of human factors analyses are very important and useful in accident investigations.

MORT

The most widely known management approach to accident causation is the Management Oversight and Risk Tree (MORT) system,

26

mentioned earlier in this chapter. The MORT approach links causes from the worker level up to the management level. The MORT system is widely used, although full MORT investigations are rarely used for accident investigations.

Sequence of Events Theory

This last theory is not so much a theory of accident causation as it is a theory of accident investigation. The idea is to document the sequence of events that led up to the accident, because if an accident investigator determines the correct chronological accident sequence, it will be easier to apply analytical techniques to find the causes of the accident. Some of the analytical techniques presented in this book will help you to determine an accident's sequence of events. All of them can help to validate a sequence and/or use the sequence of events to determine the causal factors.

Although it is possible to determine causal factors and recommend corrective actions without actually listing an accident's sequence of events, it is important to understand how and why the accident happened. For some types of accidents, it may be extremely difficult to determine the sequence of events. In fatalities or explosions, for example, some of the facts may be missing or impossible to find, but it is still important to discover as much of the accident sequence as possible. Even if an accident sequence is not fully understood, the investigator can record some of the steps in the sequence and use them to develop tests or engineering experiments to discover the rest.

Suppose, for example, that an explosion occurred at your plant, and you know exactly what happened until two minutes before the explosion. You can perform experiments to try to learn how the explosion could have been initiated in only two minutes, and that data may be crucial to the investigation. It is important to try to find as much data and discover as much of the accident sequence as possible even if you cannot find everything.

Summary

Several accident theories have come and gone as modern safety practices have evolved. Through the years, many of these theories have been modified from their original form. These theories have shaped the way safety professionals look at problems in today's workplace. The original theories are responsible for much of the terminology and many of the accident investigation techniques we use today.

Many of the accident theories discussed in this chapter can be used not only to find out how an accident occurred, but also to help prevent accidents. This book concentrates on the multiple causation theory and finding the sequence of events of an accident in order to find out what happened and how to prevent it.

REVIEW QUESTIONS

1. What is the Accident Ratio Study and what does each level represent?

2. According to the Accident Ratio Study, what level should we look at to make the most impact on safety?

3. Who first came up with the domino theory and what were the five labeled dominos?

4. Which domino theory has essentially become a separate theory?

5. Do most accidents have more than one causal factor? What theory is used if more than one causal factor is involved?

6. Think of an accident that you have been associated with. Use two of the accident causation theories described in this chapter and show how each could be applied to the accident.

CHAPTER 3

Using the Analytical Approach to Investigate Accidents

What is *analysis,* and how can it be used in accident investigations? Analysis is a systematic and exhaustive process used to determine what is unknown about an accident by examining all of the known facts or circumstances surrounding it. As a result of an accident analysis, the analyst will know as much as possible about what caused the accident and will be able to recommend corrective actions.

In taking an *analytical approach* to accident investigation, the investigator interviews people involved with the accident, takes photographs, and uses other investigative techniques to analyze an accident. In this fact-gathering process, the investigator develops scenarios that help to reveal what happened before and during the accident. This is the *accident sequence.* The events in the accident sequence that are deemed to have been causes or significant factors are called the *causal factors.*

The Phases of an Accident Investigation

Accident investigations are usually conducted in three phases: the investigative phase, the analytical phase, and the recommendation phase, as illustrated in Exhibit 3.1. These three phases are equally important, and if one of them is not performed thoroughly, the investigation process is weakened. It is difficult to analyze the evidence

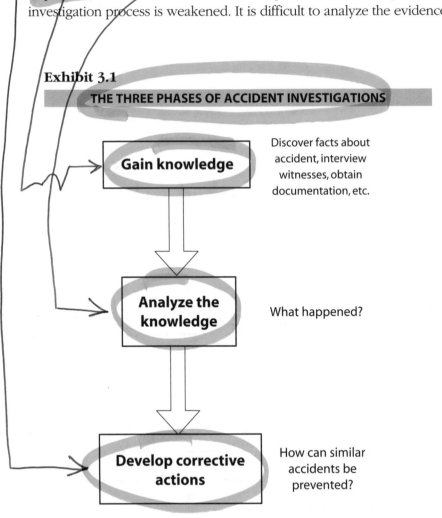

Exhibit 3.1

THE THREE PHASES OF ACCIDENT INVESTIGATIONS

Gain knowledge — Discover facts about accident, interview witnesses, obtain documentation, etc.

Analyze the knowledge — What happened?

Develop corrective actions — How can similar accidents be prevented?

from the accident if the investigation is not thorough, and it is difficult to determine corrective actions if the accident sequence and causal factors have not been identified. Unfortunately, the investigative phase seems to be left out of many "investigations," which makes it difficult if not impossible to conduct a proper analysis of the accident.

Many safety professionals compare accident investigation to the problem-solving process. As in that process, the accident investigator defines a problem, gathers data, analyzes the facts, and determines and evaluates solutions (Handley 2000).

The analytical approach establishes consistency in and lends validity to the accident investigation process. Training in analytical techniques also helps investigators to determine how much they need to find out about an accident and how much interviewing and data collection are necessary.

Thinking Analytically

During an accident investigation, it is necessary to break down the events surrounding the accident into workable pieces and dissect each one to determine whether it is significant. This requires structured thinking, a process that does not come naturally to everyone. Studying the techniques described in Part III of this book will help you to structure your thought processes and learn to systematically break down an accident.

An accident investigator must use a structured process to develop the accident sequence and a systematic and exhaustive approach to analyze evidence and determine causal factors. The analytical phase of accident investigation starts with discovering facts about the accident and using them to determine the accident sequence, and from the sequence deriving the causal factors. This systematic process eventually enables the investigator to determine corrective actions that will not only prevent recurrence of the accident, but also prevent other accidents in the future.

Root Causes and Root Cause Analysis

Safety professionals disagree about how many "root causes" there should be in an accident and even about what a root cause is. Root cause analysis is more of a process than an investigative tool or analytical tool.

Levels of Root Causes

Safety professionals agree that it is important to uncover the root causes of an accident, but everyone in the safety profession seems to have a different view about what constitutes a root cause and at what levels root causes exist. Suppose, for example, that while a worker is hammering, the hammer head comes loose, flies off the handle, and hits another worker. One investigator might say that the root cause of this accident was at the worker level. Another might examine the same accident and find that the hammer broke because proper tool maintenance procedures were not followed, so the root cause was at the management level. There are many levels of accountability, from the worker level to supervisory, management, and even corporate or program development levels. The philosophy of this book is that accident investigators must analyze events at *all* levels to determine the causes of the accident as well as recommend corrective actions.

Some safety professionals distinguish between "root causes" and "direct causes." In the hammer example above, the **direct cause** is an *engineering failure*—the hammer came apart. The **root cause** is what allowed the engineering failure to take place—in this case, *management's failure* to make sure tool inspections were being carried out. In the same example, an investigator might have identified another **direct cause**—*worker failure*—if the worker was using the hammer to do something it was not intended to do. In this case the **root cause** would be *supervisory failure* if the supervisor failed to notice that the worker was using the hammer improperly. This book discusses all of an accident's **causal factors** and **corrective actions** that may be taken at every level.

The Many Meanings of "Root Cause"

One problem with using the root cause concept is that the term "root cause" has many meanings among safety professionals. It may be defined as the first cause of an accident, the last cause of an accident, the cause that if corrected would have prevented an accident, the cause that involves management systems, the cause that started the accident sequence, or the cause that would have prevented the accident if it had not happened. These various definitions reduce the effectiveness of the term "root cause."

Some companies even have a list of possible root causes and designate one of them as the root cause of each accident. Some people call this "dial-a-cause." It allows safety professionals to make excellent charts and graphs for studying trends, but the accident itself tends to disappear while the root cause becomes the emphasis of the investigation. Many of the root causes in such a system boil down to either human error or management system failure, and it is difficult to recommend corrective actions based on such broad categories. This superficial approach obviously prevents a systematic and exhaustive process of discovering the causes of an accident. Our employees are worth more effort than this.

Ranking Root Causes

Some companies rank the root causes identified during an investigation in order of importance. This writer believes that corrective actions can be prioritized, but that causes should not be ranked.

Layered Investigations

In *Learning from Accidents in Industry,* Trevor Kletz describes an approach to accident analysis that uses *layered investigation,* which is helpful when it is important to keep types of causes separate (Kletz 1988). Kletz would say, in the hammer example, that if the accident happened because of a systemic management problem (management did not require periodic tool inspections), then an engineering failure (the hammer breaking) is the *cause* of the accident, not the *causal factor.* The causal factor is management's lack of supervision of the safety program. Even if the engineering failure is corrected, another failure will occur unless the management problem is resolved.

In layered investigations, the investigator tries to identify *all* of the causal factors instead of just the obvious ones. This method, if used with analytical techniques, will create a deeper analysis of the facts and allow the investigator to determine additional levels or "layers" of recommendations or corrective actions—a multilayered solution to the problem (Kletz 1988)(Crowl and Louvar 1990).

From Causes to Recommendations

Fixing a problem or problems is the main focus of accident investigation. Many accident investigators spend too much time finding the cause, and not enough time fixing the cause.

The basic approach to investigating accidents is to link facts, analysis, causal factors, and corrective actions. First collect the evidence and discover the facts of the accident. Then you analyze the facts to determine the accident sequence. Once the sequence of events is determined, you can tell which events are causal factors. And once you have found the causal factors, you can find corresponding corrective actions to fix the problems. This linkage among facts, analysis, causal factors, and corrective actions is crucial to the prevention of future accidents.

Summary

Although they are reactive rather than proactive, accident investigations can provide excellent chances to update and audit your safety program to ensure that it is performing effectively at all levels. In order to ensure that causal factors are found and problems are discovered, investigators must use a systematic and exhaustive thought process to determine the accident sequence, causal factors, and corrective actions.

REVIEW QUESTIONS

1. What are the three phases of accident investigation and why is each important?

2. What is wrong with using the term "root cause" in an accident investigation?

3. Why is it as important to spend adequate time on corrective actions?

4. Pick a common task such as mowing the lawn, cooking a meal, or driving a car, and analyze each step of the process. Focus on breaking down each process into a sequence of events and tell what happens at each step.

5. Pick a common appliance such as a hair dryer, blender, or coffee maker, and analyze each of its components. Focus on trying to find out the role of each component.

Part II

ORGANIZING THE INVESTIGATION

Before you determine causal factors and corrective actions, you must organize the accident investigation by gathering the information you will need to proceed. You must record facts, collect and preserve evidence, interview witnesses, search documents, take photographs, and conduct tests. If you omit any of these steps, your investigation may not be complete.

In one respect, an accident investigation is like a jigsaw puzzle. When you try to solve a jigsaw puzzle and you do not find all of the pieces, you are not able to complete the picture. When you perform an accident investigation, you start by trying to find all the pieces of evidence. From the evidence, you can determine the facts of the accident. If you do not determine all of the facts, your investigation will be incomplete. After you have ascertained the facts, you will continue with the analytical process of breaking down information to determine the accident sequence and the causal factors, just as once you have found all of the pieces of a puzzle, you can put the pieces together to make the picture whole.

Objectives for Part II:

- Be familiar with various types of evidence.
- Know how to preserve and collect evidence.

- Understand the goal of an accident investigation interview.
- Know when to stop collecting evidence.
- Understand why causal analysis is so important in the accident investigation process.
- Understand the analytical process of determining what happened and preventing it from happening again.

CHAPTER 4

Investigative Techniques

In order to perform an effective accident investigation, you must collect evidence and gather facts. Although the purpose of an accident investigation is not to assess blame and an accident investigation is not a legal proceeding, some legal-sounding terms are used during the first, or *investigative* phase of an investigation. (Remember that the three parts of an accident investigation are the *investigative phase*, the *analytical phase,* and the *recommendation phase.*) Any technique used to collect evidence and obtain facts or knowledge about the accident is called an *investigative* technique. The facts discovered and the accident sequence derived from them are used for the *analytical* phase of the investigation.

Are You Ready for an Accident?

Of course nobody is ever "ready" for an accident, but it is important to be prepared and have the right investigation tools on hand in case an accident happens. The four most important components of an accident investigation program are a formal written accident investigation policy, training in emergency response, training in accident investigation, and an accident investigation kit. Exhibit 4.1 outlines the accident investigation necessities.

Formal Written Accident Investigation Policy

This policy states the purposes of reporting accidents and investigating accidents. Important parts of the policy are:

- A statement letting employees know that all accidents must be reported through the proper channels and that the purpose of an accident investigation is not to place blame.

- A description of the purpose of an accident investigation.

- An explanation of how causal factors and corrective actions are determined.

Exhibit 4.1

ACCIDENT INVESTIGATION PREPARATION TOOLS	
1. **Formal written policy**	A policy that states the reporting process, accident investigation goals, and process of accident investigations.
2. **Emergency response plan and training**	All facilities should have an emergency response plan. While all facilities may not need a dedicated medical staff, they do need trained emergency responders who are prepared to respond to an emergency, administer care, and prevent more damage from being done.
3. **Accident investigation training**	All employees should be trained on how to report accidents and near misses. Employees and supervisors conducting accident investigations should be trained in accident investigation techniques.
4. **Accident investigation kit**	An accident investigation kit is a combination of tools and equipment that aids the accident investigator. It can range from a simple form and a camera to a full setup with tools and equipment. The kit enables the investigator to have all of the equipment he or she needs to start an investigation as soon as an accident occurs.

Emergency Response Plan and Training

The emergency response plan should emphasize fast care and rescue while minimizing the harm to other employees and the emergency responders. In larger companies, emergency response teams, fire personnel, medical personnel, and other first responders are trained to respond to accidents. Although smaller plants do not usually have dedicated emergency response teams, their employees also need to be prepared for accidents. Preparation can be in the form of training in CPR (cardiopulmonary resuscitation) and first aid as well as in evacuation and shutdown procedures.

Accident Investigation Training

The first part of accident investigation training involves all employees—everyone should understand the purpose of an accident investigation and the importance of reporting all accidents. If accidents are not reported, there is no avenue for finding and correcting problems in the safety program.

The second part involves only the people who will be conducting investigations. The company must ensure that they have the knowledge to perform adequately. Training courses on interviewing techniques, analytical techniques, causal analysis, and other aspects of investigation are available.

Accident Investigation Kit

Accident investigation kits can contain materials ranging from comprehensive—tools, personal protective equipment, cameras, tape measures, gloves, lights, security tape, tweezers, evidence bags, and other equipment—to simple—a pair of gloves, a clipboard, accident forms, and barricade tape. Exhibit 4.2 lists the contents of a typical accident investigation kit (DOE 1999). With a kit ready and waiting, an investigator can react to accidents quickly.

Exhibit 4.2

TYPICAL ACCIDENT INVESTIGATION KIT	
INVESTIGATIVE TOOLS	**ADMINISTRATIVE AND RECORDING TOOLS**
• Barricade tape	• Camera
• Cones	• Graph paper
• Tape measure	• Witness statement forms
• Flashlights/spotlights	• Notepad and clipboard
• Evidence tags	• Analytical technique forms
• Evidence bags	• Copy of the accident investigation policy
• Tweezers	
• Gloves (latex and work)	
• Personal protective equipment	
• Binoculars	

Adapted from DOE 1999

Emergency Response Actions

After an accident is reported, the first part of the accident investigation involves actions taken by the emergency response personnel. These should include:

- **Securing the scene.** This could mean turning machines off, cutting power, pulling alarms, etc. The intent is to minimize adverse effects to other employees in the plant.

- **Providing care to the injured.** One way to do this is to remove the injured person from the scene and take him or her to a medical facility. This is usually done if the person is still in a hazardous environment. If there is no danger of further injury or if there is any suspicion of back or neck injuries, it is best to leave the person at the scene until medical personnel and equipment arrive to transport him or her properly to a medical facility.

Rendering aid to an injured worker should be done only by properly trained emergency response personnel and medical personnel. Aid given by an untrained (albeit well-intentioned) person could cause additional harm.

Those providing first aid must be aware of the dangers of bloodborne pathogens and take appropriate precautions to avoid coming into contact with blood or body fluids. This means that blood and body fluids must be treated as if they are known to carry infectious pathogens. Controls, including work practice controls and personal protective equipment (gloves, masks, etc.) should be used to not only minimize exposure to emergency workers, but also to prevent other employees from having contact with these substances (U.S. Department of Labor 2003). These controls should be mandated by the company. For instance, if blood at the accident scene is known to be infectious, any worker having contact with the blood should be vaccinated against hepatitis.

Preservation of Evidence

Preserving evidence at an accident scene is an important part of accident investigation, although it must not get in the way of providing care to the injured. Securing the scene and keeping people from contaminating evidence is important in determining both lower-level causes and system failures.

How to Protect the Accident Site from Tampering and Contamination

- **Cordon off the area.** Prevent people from stepping into it or moving anything in or out of the scene.
- **Photograph the scene.** Take pictures as soon as possible after the accident, as it may be difficult to maintain the scene as it was at the time of the accident. This is especially true with accidents that occur outdoors, where wind, rain or snow can alter evidence.

Even in an indoor situation, pictures might be the only way to tell whether evidence has been tampered with or otherwise altered.

- **Interview emergency response personnel as soon as possible.** If actions of the emergency response team contaminate evidence, interview them as soon as possible after the accident while their recollection of the accident site is fresh. For example, suppose a worker is injured in an electrical accident while working on a machine. Upon arriving at the scene, the emergency responder immediately turns off the power (disconnect) to the machine. It is vital for the investigator to determine the position of the disconnect when the accident occurred, and a quick interview with the emergency responder could obtain that information. Whenever you interview emergency personnel, be sure to ask whether they moved anything at the accident scene.

- **Assess the evidence.** What evidence is there? Has any evidence been moved? Make a list of eyewitnesses, equipment and material involved and the environmental factors present when the accident occurred—time, temperature, dampness, humidity, etc.

- **Draw a picture or diagram of the scene.** Use graph paper to show the locations of the relevant items noted on your list of evidence from the scene. This will help to preserve the scene in your mind.

Types of Evidence (the Four P's)

Evidence is anything that can be used to gain knowledge or facts about the accident. There are four types of evidence: *physical, paper, people,* and *photographic.* Each type has its strengths and weaknesses. From these types of evidence, the facts of the accident are discovered. In all investigations, there can be an almost endless stream of evidence. The accident investigator must not waste his or her time analyzing evidence that has no bearing on the accident sequence or cause of the accident. The types of evidence are listed in Exhibit 4.3.

Exhibit 4.3

TYPES OF EVIDENCE

Physical Evidence—Hardware and solid material related to the accident.

Paper Evidence—Any type of written documentation related to the accident.

People Evidence—The evidence that is gathered from people, usually in the form of statements or interviews.

Photographic or Picture Evidence—Media that can document the scene and transfer knowledge.

Physical Evidence

Physical evidence is the hardware and solid material related to an accident. It can be extremely large—such as buildings, airplanes, and equipment—or small—such as debris, parts, and tools (DOE 1999). When you are documenting evidence, note the position of equipment, areas of equipment failure, and the location of debris, fracture pieces, and other solid material that could help to determine the accident's causal factors. (See "Gathering Physical Evidence" later in this chapter for more information.)

Paper Evidence

Paper evidence is any type of written documentation that is related to the accident, such as policies, procedures, training records, maintenance records, accident records, job safety analyses, analysis results, training curriculums, and spreadsheets. You can use any type of documentation that is relevant to the accident to try to find systemic problems in the safety program. (See "Gathering Paper Evidence" later in this chapter for more information.)

People Evidence

People evidence is usually in the form of statements or interviews from witnesses or others involved in the accident. A *statement* is a written description of what the person saw regarding the accident.

Some companies have special statement forms, but a statement may simply be written on a blank sheet of paper. It is important, when asking people to write witness statements, to ask them to explain in detail what happened from their point of view. An *interview* is done in a question-and-answer format; the investigator asks people questions to gain information about the accident.

Photograph or Picture Evidence

Photographs may not provide as much knowledge about an accident as the other three types of evidence do, but they are a valuable means of documenting and transferring knowledge to the accident investigator. (See "Gathering Photographic Evidence" later in this chapter for more information.)

Gathering Evidence

Gathering Physical Evidence

Physical evidence is broken into three categories: *visual evidence, testing evidence,* and *placement (puzzle) evidence.*

- **Visual evidence** includes information that can be gathered by looking at the scene, such as whether a power switch is on or off.

- **Testing evidence** must be analyzed in a laboratory—for example, if a steel beam broke and caused an accident, a lab test may be able to tell whether it broke because of a defect. This type of physical evidence usually requires the help of a subject matter expert.

- **Placement or puzzle evidence** is evidence that has broken into pieces or exploded and must be painstakingly reassembled into its original form in order to determine how the accident occurred. This is done when investigating airplane and automobile crashes and other accidents where pieces are scattered.

Tips on Gathering Physical Evidence

All physical evidence at the scene should be examined, including equipment, tools, electrical/power sources, debris, personal protective equipment, and clothing.

- **Examine the equipment, tools, debris, and solid matter** involved in an accident to determine their positions and failure points. Laboratories can perform failure analyses, structural analyses, modeling, burn tests, and many other types of tests on pieces of evidence to determine additional failure, fatigue, chemical properties, structural properties, and robustness. Other types of tests are discussed in Chapter 10.

- **Use graph paper** to sketch the accident scene, and note positions of equipment and tools.

- **Note cracks, dents, broken parts, defects, failures, and make a detailed list of mechanical parts** as you analyze each piece of evidence. Hire a consultant or expert to conduct the analysis if you don't have the expertise.

- **Measure equipment and distances between pieces of physical evidence.**

- **Take universal precautions to eliminate exposure to blood or body fluids** if they are present (U.S. Department of Labor 2003).

- **Note failure of clothing or personal protective equipment.**

- **Note the lack of personal protective equipment or equipment guards** if applicable.

Gathering Paper Evidence

Examining paper evidence is very time-consuming. You will need to look at many types of paper records to determine whether they are relevant to the accident. It is important to study paper evidence to see how your organization conducts business and handles documents. Any information that is documented on paper, including e-mails, notes, and memos, can be used as evidence, but remember to use the information to find causes and not to point blame. Paper evidence is the least likely of the "four P's" to be damaged or contaminated. Thus, it is not as important to gather these documents in the first stages of the investigation.

- **Start with lower-level or worker-level procedures and policies** for the task involved in the accident.

- **Next examine supervisory- or management-level training records, equipment maintenance records, and accident records.** Check training records to see whether appropriate training was provided and was up-to-date, and maintenance records to determine whether regular maintenance and service was provided. Calculate equipment failure rates. Check accident records to see whether similar accidents or near misses have occurred.

- **Finally examine higher-level documents** such as corporate policies, audits, and inspection reports and analyze them if you are investigating a major accident.

A note of caution: Companies generate an abundance of paper, and you do not need to sift through endless e-mails and notes to try to find a needle in the haystack. Use paper evidence to accompany and support the other forms of evidence and to structure the facts of the investigation.

Gathering People Evidence

People evidence usually takes the form of witness statements and interviews.

Witness Statements

Initiate witness statements as soon as possible after the accident, as people tend to forget what they saw over time, or their perceptions change as they interact with other people. A witness statement is simply a written statement of what happened. It is important to ask witnesses to include in their statements what they think happened and what they think could have prevented the accident. (If you create a witness statement form, include these questions.) Witnesses may have excellent ideas about how to prevent the type of accident being investigated from recurring.

Interviews

Interviewing is a unique skill and a difficult one to master. Witnesses should be interviewed as soon as possible after the accident, but for the injured individual, medical care should take precedence over interviews.

It is important to hear everyone's view of the accident. Interview each person separately so interviewees are not influenced by what others are saying. It is also important, but sometimes impossible, to prevent the witnesses from talking to each other before the interviews.

One of the most important decisions to be made about interviewing is whom to interview and how many people to interview. There is not a simple answer. If you do not interview enough people, you will not obtain enough evidence; if you interview too many, there is more paperwork, it takes more time, and possibly there will be too much evidence to sort through. Although each accident is different, here are some general guidelines: Interview all eyewitnesses, and then choose other people—workers, supervisors, safety personnel, management personnel, maintenance personnel—who may be able to lend facts and knowledge to your investigation.

Interviews are a necessary part of accident investigations, but obtaining useful information from people can be difficult. Human beings can perceive events incorrectly, or mislead, lie, or exaggerate the facts. However, people can also be correct, sincere, and helpful. How you conduct the interview can make a difference in the validity of the information you obtain.

Interviewing Tips

- **Tell people why they are being interviewed.** Put them at ease, and make sure they understand the purpose of the interview and the purpose of the accident investigation.

- **Start with an open-ended question instead of a multitude of quick questions.** If you ask short, quick questions, it may seem like you are conducting a legal interrogation. Let them tell the story of what happened.

- **Choose the interview site carefully.** This is an important variable. The best site is a place that puts the interviewee at ease. The worst place is the supervisor's or boss's office. A neutral place is best. The scene of the accident may even be acceptable. An advantage of interviewing at the accident scene is that it is easy for both you and the person you are interviewing to point out positions and exact locations. A disadvantage is that it could be emotional for the interviewee (Vincoli 1994)(Bird and Germain 1985).

- **Make notes and repeat important points.** This is important to ensure that you are documenting the interviewee's information correctly.

- **At the end of each interview, end on a positive note** and thank people for their time and help in the accident investigation.

- **Ask interviewees what they think caused the accident and what they think could have prevented it.** While the investigative phase of the accident is the place to gather evidence and facts, not conclusions, it is still a good idea to let interviewees comment on possible causal relationships and preventive measures. Keep in mind, of course, that their comments may be based on a limited perspective and may be affected by a reluctance to criticize those above them. But it is still helpful to give witnesses a voice in the investigation. This will empower them and make them feel like an important part of the accident investigation process.

- **Obtain contact information** in case you need to ask follow-up questions.

- **Do not interview people with the notion that you must distinguish truths from the lies.** Most employees are truthful; lying is the exception. What may happen, however, is that once people start talking about the accident, a group consensus may develop and everyone may adopt that version of what happened.

- **Practice interviewing.** Interviewing is a skill, and every interview is different. The best way to improve your interviewing skills is to practice.

Exhibit 4.4 lists some good interviewing skills.

Gathering Photographic Evidence

Photographs are sometimes not considered a form of evidence, but they can be an important part of an accident investigation. Many accident investigators hire a professional photographer or appoint one person in the company to photograph accident scenes. A few

Exhibit 4.4

GOOD INTERVIEWING SKILLS	
ESTABLISH COMMUNICATIONS	**ASK QUESTIONS**
• Explain the purpose of the interview.	• Ask open-ended questions to get the interviewee's view of the accident.
• Explain the purpose of the accident investigation.	• Have specific questions ready.
• Do not rush the interview.	• Obtain specific times and dates for each event.
• Be friendly and professional.	
• Do not start with rapid-fire questions.	• Always ask what caused the accident and what could have prevented it.
• Make the interviewee feel that he or she is an important part of the investigation process.	• Always end positively.
• Do not judge, become angry, refute, or suggest.	
• Obtain the interviewee's job title, experience, education, training, etc.	

Adapted from OSHA Institute 1995

good photographs are better than many bad photographs, but you must take enough photographs so that a person who has not seen the accident site can understand the accident sequence.

It is a good idea to take photographs of the accident scene before you move anything. It is even better to videotape the area before, during, and after moving an object. Doing this could be important in discovering information about controls, disconnects, and systems component failures. Be sure to photograph anything that will be removed or will disappear eventually, such as tire tracks, footprints, and spills.

Many modern digital cameras can take both still pictures and videos. It can be useful to e-mail photos of a particular accident to colleagues at other locations to help them prevent the same type of accident in their facilities. It is also easy to incorporate digital pictures into an accident investigation report.

Photo Tips

- Be sure to take some "big picture" photos—overall pictures of the entire accident scene. They are important to show the environment and relationships and distances between all people and equipment in the accident.

- Include a reference object in the picture if the purpose of the photograph is to show relationships. This way the general sizes of items in the picture will be obvious. A good reference object for small items is a 12-inch ruler or a pen or pencil. A good reference object for a larger item is a person standing next to the item.

- Keep a photo log to identify pictures and note their purpose. The minimum information to include for each picture is the photo number, the object or purpose of the photo, the location the picture was taken from, the direction of the shot, and the time the picture was taken.

When to Stop Collecting Evidence

The time to stop evidence collection varies depending on the accident's complexity. Evidence collection should continue until you have enough information to document the accident sequence, determine causal factors, and develop corrective actions. In many accidents it may seem that all of the facts and knowledge will never be determined, but at some point you must stop collecting evidence and start analyzing and determining corrective actions.

In most accident investigations, evidence collection continues until the accident sequence is determined. At that point, analytical techniques are used to determine the causal factors and corrective actions. However, if additional facts are needed, evidence collection can be re-initiated.

For small accidents and near misses, all evidence collection can be documented on an accident investigation form. This form is used to record witness statements, the results of evidence collection and interviews, documented facts, causal factors, and corrective actions.

Summary

It is important to be prepared for an accident investigation before an accident happens. Companies must prepare a written accident investigation policy; have an emergency response plan; train employees in emergency response, accident reporting, and accident investigation; and put together an accident investigation kit. Accident investigators must collect all evidence pertaining to the accident, including physical, paper, people, and photographic evidence. All evidence collected must be preserved to ensure the accuracy of the investigation.

The investigative phase of the accident investigation is the part that will find the evidence of the accident. The facts of the accident are ascertained from the evidence that is collected. Evidence collection should continue until the accident sequence is determined.

REVIEW QUESTIONS

1. What needs to be in place before an accident occurs?

2. What kind of training needs to be provided?

3. What are the four types of evidence? Describe each type.

4. Why is it important to obtain witness statements as soon as possible after an accident and before witnesses have discussions among themselves?

5. What is a "big picture" photograph?

6. There has just been a construction accident at your plant involving a crane picking up a load of steel beams. A crane operator, two laborers, and a foreman were at the job site. You are to interview these four workers. List some questions that you would ask each worker.

7. Basing your answer on the same crane accident, make a list of what you would like to collect as evidence. Make a list of all physical, paper, people, and photograph evidence you would need.

CHAPTER 5

The Analytical Process

An accident investigation is the process of breaking down information into pieces until the investigator understands what happened; then he or she can analyze the pieces to determine ways to prevent the accident from recurring. Asking "why" is a crucial first step in discovering the causal factors of an accident.

Causal Analysis

Once the evidence from an accident is gathered, you must discover the accident sequence, and once you know the sequence, causal analysis—the process of determining the causal factors—can begin. (Senecal and Burke 1994). The goal of causal analysis is to find all of the causes including the systemic causes—not just the immediate or superficial causes. If only the superficial causes are found and dealt with, the same accident could happen again with a different employee.

One of the problems accident investigators sometimes have is knowing when to stop searching for causes. Many accident investigators have used the "Five Whys" technique to find causes. This is simply asking "Why?" five times to get to the root of a problem.

For example, suppose John was working outdoors carrying pipes from one location to another when a pipe fell on his foot. Here are five "Why?" questions the investigator could ask John, each going deeper into the cause of the accident:

> Investigator: John, why did the pipe fall on your foot?
>
> John: I dropped it.
>
> Investigator: Why did you drop it?
>
> John: It slipped out of my hand.
>
> Investigator: Why did it slip?
>
> John: It was wet.
>
> Investigator: Why was it wet?
>
> John: The pipes were sitting in a pool of water.
>
> Investigator: Why were they sitting in water?
>
> John: It rained earlier today.

(Obviously, the questioning process in this case has only begun.)

Causal analysis is a process in which an investigator analyzes, probes, discovers, ponders, and uses scenarios, facts, tests, and assumptions to determine what caused an accident. Causes and causal factors can exist at many levels—worker, equipment (failure or hazard), supervisor, management, management systems (policies and procedures), and even corporate culture, philosophy, and style. Lower-level causes are usually more specific to one particular accident, but they are still important to list and fix. In fact, problems at the lowest level can lead to worthwhile engineering and equipment corrections that solve a problem or eliminate a hazard. Upper-level causal factors are more difficult to fix, but doing so will affect a broader range of people and situations and help to prevent future accidents (DOE 1999). Exhibit 5.1 displays the levels of accountability for accident investigations.

Exhibit 5.1

LEVELS OF ACCOUNTABILITY	
1. Worker or equipment level	This is the lowest level of accountability. At the worker level work is performed and equipment operates. Causal factors in this area include equipment failures, inadequate training, inexperience, and what many consider human error (which would include training, experience, etc.).
2. Supervisor level	People at this level describe how work is to be done. Causal factors often include inadequate handling of job safety analyses, communication, or scheduling, and lack of proper supervision.
3. Management level	Management level dictates policies and procedures. Causal factors at this level are usually related to budget issues, communication, and policies/procedures.
4. Corporate level	This highest level dictates the culture, philosophy, and style of the company. If problems are found and corrected at this level, many accidents can be prevented.

Causal Analysis Example

An accident occurred when a worker did not use a lock and tag to isolate a piece of equipment and keep the electricity out.

A lower-level causal factor is that the worker failed to use the proper lockout/tagout procedure to isolate the energy. A higher-level factor could be that management did not enforce or have a policy on lockout/tagout. If the lower-level problem is fixed—the worker is trained on lockout/tagout procedures and given a lock and tag—*that* worker probably will not have another accident. However, if management develops a policy of training *all* workers in lockout/tagout procedures, many similar accidents can be prevented.

With this type of accident, a causal factor may also exist at the corporate level if upper management failed to audit the plant's procedures and therefore did not find out that the plant lacked lockout/tagout policies. If upper management started performing policy audits, many more types of accidents caused by failure to follow policy or procedure—not just electrical and lockout/tagout accidents—could be avoided.

This example demonstrates the importance of analyzing an accident at *all levels*. If you investigate only at the lower levels you may miss some of the causal factors—and thus the corrective actions—at the higher levels. Making changes at higher levels is more complex than making them at lower levels: It is difficult to change a company's culture, philosophy, or style. This does not mean that you should avoid investigating high-level causal factors—each level of accountability is important—but everyone should be aware that the only corrective action that is effective is one that is initiated and supported by the appropriate decision-makers.

Hazards vs. Failures

As you investigate accidents, it is important to distinguish between hazards and failures. A *hazard* is something that has the potential to cause injury, and hazards are correctable. Examples of hazards are a sharp table edge or a pool of grease on the floor.

A *failure* is something that goes wrong with personnel, equipment, or the environment (Ferry 1981). A failure may or may not have the potential to cause injury. If it does, it is also considered a hazard. A dead battery in an automobile is an example of a failure that is not a hazard; ordinarily it would not cause an accident. However, an automobile tire that fails and blows out while someone is driving is considered a hazard as well as a failure, because the failure could cause an accident.

Failures are usually caused by faulty design, a defect, inadequate maintenance, limits that were exceeded, or environmental effects.

Analytical Techniques

Many accident investigation techniques were derived from system safety techniques that were developed to analyze equipment design failures and hazards. These types of techniques are used by the Department of Defense and Department of Energy (Vincoli 1994).

There are four main accident investigation techniques. They are introduced here and will be examined in depth in the next part of this book:

- events and causal factors analysis
- change analysis
- barrier analysis
- analytical trees

Each technique analyzes a different type of problem, and each has strengths and weaknesses. The techniques are broad enough in scope to handle small incidents as well as major catastrophes. Using several techniques in an investigation ensures accuracy, consistency, and validity and helps investigators to obtain more information about the accident sequence, be more accurate and precise, and share investigative responsibilities with others. It is also possible for the results of different techniques to validate each other. These techniques must not be used mechanically or without consideration of the accident sequence and circumstances (DOE 1999).

A flowchart of analytical techniques is illustrated in Exhibit 5.2.

Benefits of Using Analytical Techniques

- If you do not use analytical techniques, it is very easy to find only lower-level causal factors and miss the systemic factors.
- Using analytical techniques for every accident investigation lends consistency to your safety program.

Exhibit 5.2

ANALYTICAL TECHNIQUES FLOWCHART

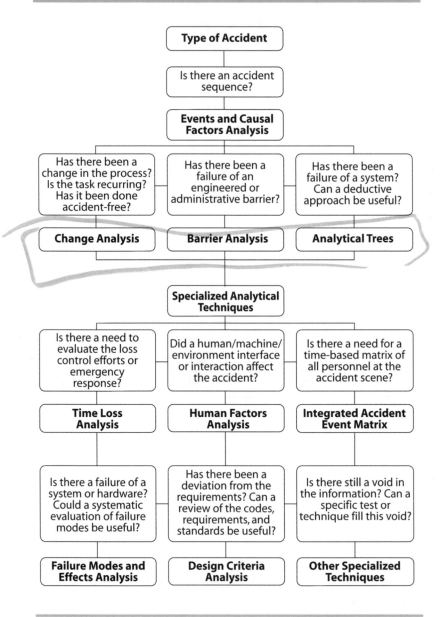

Adapted from OSHA Institute 1995

- Analytical techniques will help you to make a smooth and consistent transition from facts to causal factors.

- The thoroughness of the analytical techniques will give you confidence that your investigation determined what really happened and that your recommendations will prevent future accidents.

Summary

The events or circumstances that contribute to an accident are called causal factors. Correction of these causal factors at whatever level they may occur is what ensures that a particular incident will not recur. When using analytical techniques, investigators must be able to distinguish between hazards and failures. Using causal analysis and analytical techniques will make the investigation more effective.

REVIEW QUESTIONS

1. What is a causal factor?

2. Describe the four levels of accountability.

3. What is the difference between a hazard and a failure?

4. Why is it advisable to use more than one analytical technique to investigate an accident?

Part III

ANALYTICAL TECHNIQUES

Part III focuses on how to analyze an accident and determine what happened. It explains events and causal factors analysis, change analysis, barrier analysis, and analytical trees, as well as some other accident investigation tools and techniques.

Part III also introduces a fictional accident scenario that will be used to demonstrate techniques throughout the rest of the book, with each demonstration building on the ones before it. The scenario is not intended to fully analyze an accident but simply to demonstrate accident investigation techniques.

ACCIDENT SCENARIO

Injury: Employee fell off a ladder and suffered a broken arm and a concussion.

When: 7:45 A.M., February 5, 2003

Where: Warehouse

Accident Description: Bill, a recently hired warehouse supervisor, was hanging up a new exit sign to comply with NFPA Life Safety Code requirements. During a recent warehouse expansion, new rows had been added, and the fire inspector, during his visit the previous day, had noted that new exit signs needed to be installed. Bill wanted to correct the violation as soon as possible.

He arrived at work before his shift began—while the night shift was still stocking shelves—to hang the signs. He placed a ladder at the end of an aisle between two rows and climbed the ladder to hang the sign. A forklift driver coming down the next aisle turned the corner and hit the ladder. Bill fell and landed on his arm and head. The forklift driver was not injured. She immediately alerted her supervisor and the proper medical personnel were called.

Other Information: This was a non-recurring task. There were no written job procedures for this exact task; however there were procedures for changing light bulbs, a similar task. There were also procedures for working on ladders and procedures for working in the aisles of the warehouse. There was no discussion or review of potential hazards associated with this task. Bill's shift started at 8:00 A.M. Night shift personnel were taking their last load to the warehouse before taking the forklifts to the recharging area. Communication between the shifts and within management had always been a problem. Bill was new to supervision; he had just completed supervisor training the week before. The forklift driver was properly trained.

Objectives for Part III:

- Understand the analytical techniques used for accident investigations.
- Be able to perform an events and causal factors analysis, change analysis, barrier analysis, and analytical tree for any accident.
- Have a general working knowledge of other specialized and computerized techniques.

CHAPTER 6

Events and Causal Factors Analysis

One of the most important steps in performing a comprehensive accident investigation is documenting the accident sequence, and one of the best ways to do this is to use *events and causal factors analysis*. This technique has two parts—creating an events and causal factors *chart* and using the chart to *analyze* the accident. The events and causal factors analysis will help you to determine the accident sequence, analyze the sequence, and find the causal factors of the accident.

About Events and Causal Factors Analysis

The concept of events and causal factors analysis has been around for more than thirty years under a variety of names. The National Transportation Safety Board used a similar technique called Multilinear Event Sequences to document the events of an accident (Benner 1975) (Ferry 1981). The Department of Energy incorporated events and causal factors charting into its MORT system. In *System Safety 2000,* Joe Stephenson introduced the idea of visualizing and analyzing the chart to find causes and develop corrective actions. He called this process *causal factors analysis* (Stephenson 1991). The refinements made through the years are incorporated into the description of events and causal factors analysis discussed in this chapter.

The Events and Causal Factors
Analysis Approach

As an accident investigation progresses, more and more information is learned about the accident. Events and causal factors analysis provides a tool—the *events and causal factors chart*—for chronologically arranging this information to create a timeline of the accident. As facts are uncovered, the corresponding events and conditions are incorporated into the chart. The investigator *analyzes* the chart to find the causal factors of the accident only after *all* of the facts have been discovered. Figure 6-1 illustrates the events and causal factors analysis timeline approach.

Events and Causal Factors Charting

Some of the functions of the events and causal factors analysis chart are listed and discussed below (OSHA Institute 1995) (Department of Energy 1999):

- Graphic portrayal of the accident sequence
- Recording of events and conditions

Exhibit 6.1

EVENTS AND CAUSAL FACTORS ANALYSIS TIMELINE APPROACH

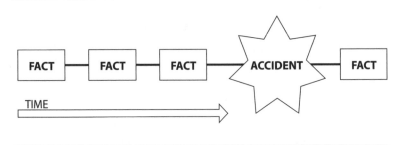

- Validation and verification of facts
- Discovery of holes in the accident sequence
- Identification of multiple causes
- Elimination of memorization as a means of documentation
- Aid in report writing
- Determination of causal factors (in the analysis part of the technique)

Graphic Portrayal of the Accident Sequence

Start constructing the chart as soon you obtain facts about the accident. Many investigators find it convenient to write information on removable adhesive notes and place them in chronological order on a wall or table. Notecards also work, but they must be taped in place. Computer programs can print an events and causal factors chart, but it is best to use them after the wall or table chart is completed.

Recording of Events and Conditions

Three types of information are recorded on an events and causal factors chart: *events* (occurrences with time and date), *conditions* (what was going on during the events), and the *accident* itself. At the top of the adhesive note for each event, write the event as a sentence with a subject and an action verb to describe the event (example: "Bill dropped the hammer."). At the bottom of the note write the time and date the event happened and the source of the information. On separate notes write conditions that existed at the time of the event. See "Documentation Procedures" later in this chapter for more information on recording events and conditions.

Validation and Verification of Facts

You may encounter conflicting information as you examine evidence and interview people. If you write on each event or condition note where you obtained the information—witness statement, interview of foreman, lockout/tagout log, plant procedures, etc.—you will have a way to decide which piece of information is valid.

Discovery of Holes in the Accident Sequence

Examining the events and causal factors chart is an excellent way to find holes in your investigation. Since the chart is in chronological time order, it is easy to tell whether information is missing. It is important to find all of the available information and facts about the accident before you start analyzing the accident sequence.

Identification of Multiple Causes

As you document the facts of the accident on the events and causal factors chart, the chart actually becomes the accident sequence, and it can be used to identify multiple causes as well as a single cause.

Elimination of Memorization as a Means of Documentation

As you start investigating an accident, you may rely on memory rather than a chart to keep track of the information you discover. However, it is extremely difficult to memorize the events and conditions for complex accidents—there is just too much information to keep track of mentally. The events and causal factors chart is a concrete way to document the facts that so that you do not depend on memorization.

Aid in Report Writing

When you write an accident investigation report, an events and causal factors chart will provide an excellent outline of the accident.

Charting Procedures

Most investigators construct charts in a secure, controlled location using removable adhesive notes or notecards taped to a wall or table. After the chart is complete, some investigators transfer the information to a specialized computer program. (See "Computerized Charts" later in this chapter.)

Charting Various Types of Events

Events

Record each event, along with the date and time it occurred and the information source, on a separate note and place the note in chronological order in the chart. Events should be written with a subject (noun) and a verb.

Assumed Events

These are events that you know must have happened but have not yet been verified. Write them on notes of a different color from those used for verified events. This will remind you that more investigation is needed.

Non-events—Events That Did Not Occur

If a worker did not place a lock and tag on an electrical panel, this is a non-event. Non-events can be important in determining causal factors. Some accident investigators do not include non-events on their charts, while others include them until all of the other information is received. Information about non-events should be captured somehow, and the chart is a good place to document it. Although they are not events, they may be cited as conditions or causal factors when the chart is analyzed.

Events That Occur Simultaneously

It is possible for two events to occur at the same time. In this case, place the second set of events and conditions directly below the first to signify that they occurred at the same time. Exhibit 6.2 displays a secondary event sequence.

Exhibit 6.2

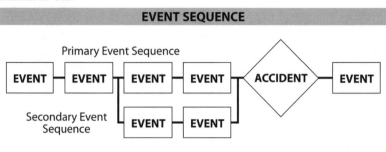

Charting Conditions

Conditions are situations related to an event, such as what caused the event to happen, what was happening during the event, or even non-events. For example, suppose that the event is that a worker turned off an electrical panel in Room A. Conditions associated with this event might be that the worker was about to service a machine (what caused the event); Room A was not well-lit because a light was burned out (what was happening during the event); and he did not place a lock and tag on the electrical panel (non-event). On the chart, use different color notes for events and conditions.

Charting the Accident

The last type of information to chart is the accident itself. Place a note on the chart (in a different color from those used for events and conditions) describing the accident along with a time and date. It is possible for events to occur both before and after an accident; usually the ones after the accident will be emergency response actions. When you look at the chart, it will be obvious where the accident falls in relation to the events and conditions leading up to and following it.

Computerized Charts

If you transfer your chart to a computer, it is customary to place events in rectangles, conditions in ovals, and accidents in diamonds. For assumed events and conditions, dashed rectangles and ovals are used. There are computer programs specifically designed to create events and causal factors charts; however, many other programs—such as PowerPoint™, Visio™, and CAD or graphic programs—can be used as well.

Exhibit 6.3 illustrates a typical event, condition, and the accident.

Exhibit 6.3

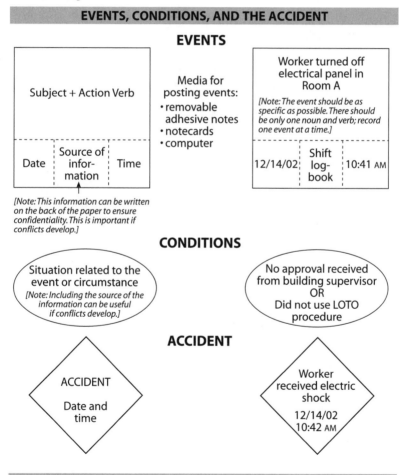

How Much Should You Include on the Chart?

The chart's effectiveness is linked to the amount of information included on it. You must sift through all of the information you receive and place all of the important events and conditions on the chart. A short example will illustrate an events and causal factors chart.

> An office worker noticed that a light bulb in the break room was burned out and decided to change the bulb himself. He found a new light bulb and a step ladder. He had one of his lunch partners hold the ladder as he climbed to the top rung. As he reached to screw in the light bulb, he fell off the ladder and broke his arm.

Exhibit 6.4 depicts an events and causal factors chart for this simple example. Note that each event note contains a sentence describing the event and the date and time of the event. The source of the information, in this case the injured worker, is omitted in this example but could be written on the back of the note. Conditions associated with the events are written on notes placed above each event note, stacking them vertically if there are several. As with event notes, source information should be written on each condition note.

Charting Tips

- **Fill your chart with information.** Do not be too concerned with charting style and correctness—just include as much information as you can.

- **Make room for your chart.** Charts for complex accidents grow from day to day as new information is received. Place adhesive event and condition notes on a wall or large table, depending on the size of the investigation. For larger investigations the notes may wrap around an entire room!

Exhibit 6.4

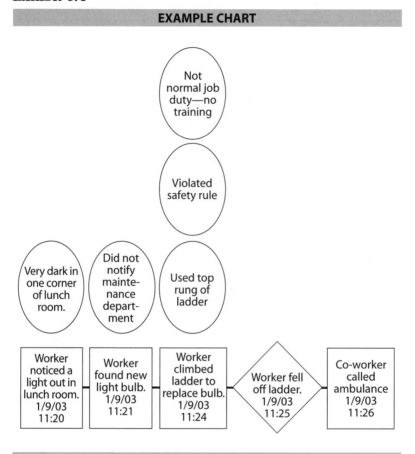

EXAMPLE CHART

- **Keep the notes sticky.** Especially in humid offices, do not depend on adhesive notes to keep sticking as they are moved to make room for others—use additional tape.

- **Leave some expansion room.** Leave some breaks in the chart for expansion to avoid having to move all of the notes every time you insert a new one. Put space between events when you think additional information will be received.

- **Mark time breaks.** For complex accidents, tape day, hour, and possibly minute markers to the wall so you can find and place notes easily.

- **Be thorough, but be aware that being thorough takes time.** For complex accidents, creating events and causal factors charts is extremely time-consuming, but the more time you take, the more thoroughly you will have investigated the accident. If all pertinent information is not included in your chart, your analysis is not representative of the entire accident sequence, and you may not discover the true causal factors of the accident.

- **Archive the chart.** Once the chart is finished and the causal factors have been analyzed, it can be taken down and the information entered into a computer. When you take the chart down, disassemble it carefully, keeping the event notes in order and the condition notes behind their corresponding event notes. If you need to revisit the chart, you will be able to reconstruct it easily. Store chart notes and computer printouts in a protected area.

- **Use the chart as the basis of a report.** You may wish to include a summary of the chart in your accident investigation report. Pick ten to fifteen events that summarize the accident sequence. The events you choose should include all of the events that were identified as causal factors. A chart like this tells the story of the accident—it gives the reader the events, conditions, and causal factors in an easily understood chronological picture. Summary charts are also very effective as management tools (Stephenson 1991).

Events and Causal Factors Analysis

Analysis of the events and conditions—a qualitative approach to visualizing the accident—begins when the chart is finished. Exhibit 6.5 portrays this part of the process. You must evaluate each event to determine its significance to the accident, asking, "What occurred? How did it occur? Why did it occur? What is its relevance? What are

Exhibit 6.5

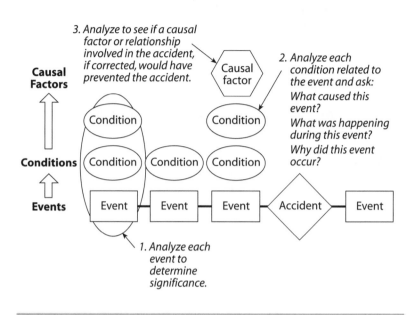

EVENTS AND CAUSAL FACTORS ANALYSIS

the circumstances surrounding it?" As you answer these questions, you will discover the accident's causal factors. It is usually best to start with the first event and proceed until you reach the accident. Do not skip events—sometimes the more obscure ones turn out to be very important. When you have finished the analysis, you may wish to distinguish the events that were causal factors with a color code or symbol such as a hexagon.

Example Scenario

In the forklift-hitting-the-ladder example given in the introduction to Part III, two accidents may be identified—the forklift hitting the ladder and the supervisor falling off the ladder. While investigating either

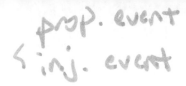

should yield the same causal factors, the one in which injury or damage is involved—in this case the supervisor falling off the ladder—is usually identified as the primary accident.

Exhibit 6.6 illustrates the first stage of the events and causal factors chart. All of the facts and information related to this accident are not

Exhibit 6.6

EVENTS AND CAUSAL ANALYSIS OF EXAMPLE SCENARIO

```
 ( Shortage of )      ( 1st )          ( No exit )
 ( warehouse  )      ( supervisory )   ( sign on new )
 ( suprevisors )      ( job )          ( aisles )

[ New wing of ]   [ Bill received ]  [ Fire
  warehouse        promotion to       inspection
  finished.        warehouse          found
  1/6/03 ]         supervisor.        violations in    /A\
                   1/23/03 ]          warehouse.
                                      2/4/03 ]
```

```
                                     ( No )
                                     ( communication )
                                     ( with night )
                                     ( supervisor )

 ( Normal shift )    ( Job not )     ( No safety )
 ( starts at 8:00 )  ( scheduled )   ( review )
                                     ( performed )

/A\ [ Bill arrived at ] [ Bill retrieved ] [ Bill walked
      work.               a ladder.          with ladder to
      2/5/03              2/5/03             end of row.      /B\
      7:35 ]              7:41 ]             2/5/03
                                            7:43 ]
```

included in this chart; other analysis methods discussed later in the book will add information and the chart will continue to grow until it includes all of the information necessary for analysis.

EVENTS AND CAUSAL ANALYSIS OF EXAMPLE SCENARIO, continued

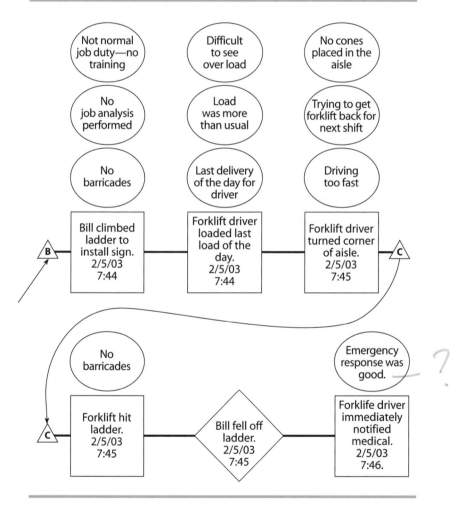

Summary

Events and causal factors analysis is a comprehensive accident investigation tool that develops the accident sequence as well as determining causal factors. The accident sequence is separated into events and conditions. The events illustrate a timeline of the accident. After a complete chart is developed from the facts of the accident, the events and conditions are analyzed and causal factors are determined. Many hours of work are needed to produce an effective events and causal factors analysis; however, the result is that accident investigators understand the accident sequence and are confident that the causal factors of the accident have been found. This technique ensures that an adequate investigation is performed and a documented accident sequence is developed. This technique answers the ultimate question for accident investigators: "Why did this accident occur?"

REVIEW QUESTIONS

1. What are the advantages of using an events and causal factors analysis to investigate an accident?

2. What analysis errors might be caused by an incorrect timeline?

3. Why is it important to document the source of each item of information?

4. When should an events and causal factors chart be started?

5. How do you display two events that occurred at the same time?

6. How do you perform the analysis portion of the event and causal factors analysis?

7. How do you make a summary chart from a completed events and causal factors chart?

8. Continue the events and causal factors chart for the example scenario (Exhibit 6.6).

CHAPTER 7

Change Analysis

A change of some sort is a major factor in most accidents. Although change is a necessary component of progress, it can also be catastrophic. Change can be planned, anticipated, or desired; it can also be unintentional or unwanted. Change analysis is a technique for analyzing the changes that led up to an accident. It can be combined with other techniques or used independently.

Change analysis can be used both reactively and proactively. When it is used reactively, the investigator looks back at the events that led up to the accident and determines the unintentional or unwanted changes that may have caused it. What was different about how the process was performed this time that caused the accident to happen? When it is used proactively, safety professionals develop scenarios that introduce a planned, anticipated, or desired change into a system and use change analysis techniques to identify potential hazards or accident situations that could arise because of the change. Change analysis can also be used to review processes or to identify the potential effects of changes before implementing a new procedure or process (Stephenson 1991)(Spear 2002). Many safety professionals use a modified change analysis process to comply with the Process Safety Management regulatory requirements for management of change.

About Change Analysis

The technique of change analysis was first used before World War II (Ferry 1981) and was perfected by Charles Kepner and Benjamin Tregoe for the U.S. Air Force in the 1950s. Bill Johnson also used this technique in the Management Oversight and Risk Tree (MORT) system developed for the Department of Energy. When using it, the investigator compares the sequence of events leading up to an accident with a similar non-accident sequence to find the causes of the accident.

 Although change analysis can be used with any accident investigation, it is most useful for accidents that happen while routine tasks are being performed. For first-aid incidents, near misses, and accidents that occur during simple tasks, change analysis may be sufficient on its own to determine what happened; it will provide enough information to determine how to prevent the sequence from developing again.

For more complex accidents, change analysis must be structured and detailed. It is not enough for the investigator to simply ask, "What changed to cause the usual sequence of events to turn into an accident sequence?" Every event that changed, including management systems events, must be analyzed in detail, and frequently other analysis methods must be used in addition to change analysis.

The Change Analysis Approach

The approach of change analysis is to compare an accident situation or sequence with a similar accident-free situation or sequence. The basic change analysis sequence is illustrated in Exhibit 7.1 and a summary of comparison methods is illustrated in Exhibit 7.2.

Types of Accident-Free Situations

It is critical to find a directly related accident-free situation or sequence to compare with the accident situation. Three types of situations can be used:

Exhibit 7.1

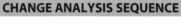
CHANGE ANALYSIS SEQUENCE

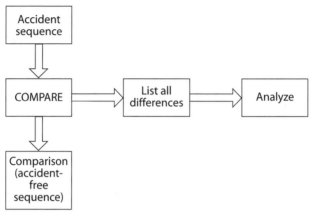

The Same Procedure as It Is Usually Performed

Ideally, the investigator is able to compare the accident sequence with the same procedure as it was performed accident-free—last week, last month, or last year. Since an accident did not occur during that situation, what was different in the sequence this time that may have contributed to the accident.

A Description of the Job as It Is Supposed to Be Performed

Comparing the accident sequence to a written description of how a task is supposed to be performed makes change analysis simple for the investigator. This process is also called Codes, Standards, and Regulations (CSR), Procedure Design Criteria Analysis, or Procedure Adherence Analysis. The investigator compares the accident sequence to the procedure, standard, or regulation and discovers where change has occurred. One problem with comparing the accident sequence to a task description sequence is that the worker involved in the accident might not actually have *changed* the usual procedure. It is possible that workers have *never* performed the job as it is described by the

Exhibit 7.2

CHANGE ANALYSIS COMPARISON METHODS	
COMPARE THE ACCIDENT SEQUENCE TO:	
1. An "accident-free" situation	How the job was performed last week, last month, or last year with no accidents.
2. Plant procedures	How the task was supposed to be performed according to company policy.
3. An "ideal" situation	How the job would be performed under ideal circumstances.

standard or procedure. If this is the case, then it was not a change but a *difference* from the described procedure that caused the accident.

A Description of the Job as It Should Be Performed

This sounds very much like the comparison in the previous paragraph, but it is subtly different. In this kind of comparison, the investigator compares the accident sequence events not with written standards but with a description of the way the task would be performed under ideal circumstances. With this method, the investigator is not comparing changes but differences between the accident sequence and the ideal sequence, since the task has probably never been performed in the ideal way. If the investigator finds a better way to perform the procedure, it can be recommended as a corrective action.

Making Thorough Comparisons

As you perform change analysis, you must compare all events and conditions involved in the accident with corresponding events and conditions in the accident-free scenario. Ask the following questions about each event: *Who was involved? What happened? When did it happen? Where did it happen? How did it happen?* Analyze each set of events and conditions and ask what changes may have occurred: Is the time or place different? Are the people involved different? On a managerial level, was it managed, controlled, reviewed, or implemented differently? (DOE 1999.) After you have made a thorough comparison, find the differences between the two sequences. In most situations, they are quite obvious. Finally, determine how that difference caused the accident.

The short example below demonstrates the change analysis approach.

> Bob had gone fishing every day for twenty years, and every day he had been able to catch fish for his lunch and dinner. One day, he did not catch any fish, and he wondered why. He compared the unsuccessful day to all of the previous successful days and found that he had used the same fishing hole and the same hook size, and had fished at the same time of day. The only difference was that he had used different bait on the unsuccessful day, so he reasoned that using different bait was the cause of his failure to catch fish.

Accident investigations will never be this easy to analyze, of course, and the analysis does not stop with finding that different bait was the reason for fishing failure. The next steps are to learn why Bob decided to change his bait and why the new bait didn't seem to attract fish. In change analysis, you must find out *all* of the changes that occurred and analyze how they affected the outcome.

Change Analysis Procedures

Change analysis is performed on a four-column worksheet (see Exhibit 7.3).

- **Column 1:** Write the accident sequence.
- **Column 2:** Write the events of a comparable accident-free sequence.
- **Column 3:** Note the differences or changes between the events in column 1 and column 2.
- **Column 4:** Analyze the differences or changes in column 3 and determine how they affected the outcome.

Exhibit 7.3

CHANGE ANALYSIS WORKSHEET			
ACCIDENT SEQUENCE	**COMPARISON SEQUENCE**	**DIFFERENCE**	**ANALYSIS**
1.	1.	1.	1.
2.	2.	2.	2.
.	.	.	.
.	.	.	.
.	.	.	.
Describe the accident sequence.	Describe a comparable sequence from an accident-free situation.	Identify the differences between the accident sequence and the comparison sequence for each step.	Analyze the differences and describe how they affected the accident.

Example Scenario

When performing change analysis, you must find an accident-free sequence to compare to the accident sequence. Although our forklift-and-ladder scenario is a non-recurring task that has no specific written description, there are procedures for using ladders and working in warehouse aisles, and changing light bulbs is similar to installing signs, so that procedure was used as the comparison sequence. Exhibit 7.4 lists only the events in the accident sequence that are different from those in the comparison sequence. After the first three columns are filled in, analyze differences between the accident sequence and the comparison sequence that could be significant to the accident. The fourth column lists several differences that had a significant impact on the accident.

Exhibit 7.3

CHANGE ANALYSIS OF EXAMPLE SCENARIO

ACCIDENT SEQUENCE	COMPARISON SEQUENCE	DIFFERENCE	ANALYSIS
1. This job did not obtain a safety review.	1. All jobs go through a safety and scheduling review.	1. No safety or scheduling review was performed.	1. A safety review was not conducted; it would have initiated the proper procedures.
2. The warehouse supervisor performed the task.	2. Maintenance workers perform maintenance tasks.	2. The proper personnel did not perform the job.	2. The workers who are familiar with the procedures did not perform the job.
3. No communication was made to the night warehouse supervisor.	3. Communication about work will go through the supervisors.	3. The work was not communicated to the night supervisor.	3. The night supervisor did not know about the job and thus did not alert the forklift drivers to potential closed aisles. Lack of communication between supervisors seems common.
4. No rows were barricaded.	4. All aisles and ends of rows are barricaded off.	4. Rows were not barricaded.	4. The forklift driver did not realize that the row was closed.

Continued on next page

CHANGE ANALYSIS OF EXAMPLE SCENARIO, continued			
ACCIDENT SEQUENCE	**COMPARISON SEQUENCE**	**DIFFERENCE**	**ANALYSIS**
5. No cones were placed in the aisles.	5. Cones are placed before the barricades to alert forklift drivers that aisles are closed.	5. No cones were placed.	5. The forklift driver was used to seeing cones placed by the maintenance department when aisles were closed.
6. The forklift driver could not clearly see in front of the forklift.	6. Forklift drivers are able to clearly see in front of the forklift.	6. The forklift was overloaded and it was difficult for the driver to see.	6. The forklift driver was in a hurry and overloaded the forklift.
7. The forklift driver was driving faster than the posted speed.	7. Forklift drivers do not exceed posted speed.	7. The forklift was going too fast.	7. The forklift driver was rushing to get through the shift.
8. The supervisor was new to the job.	8. Supervisors are experienced.	8. The supervisor was inexperienced.	8. The supervisor was new to supervision and was used to getting things done instead of using the proper procedure.

Summary

Change analysis is a simple technique for analyzing differences between the events in an accident sequence and the events in an accident-free comparison sequence. Changes are usually important factors in an accident sequence. A systematic change analysis comparing the accident sequence to a comparable accident-free sequence is valuable in finding abstract causes of accidents. Information discovered during change analysis will help prevent accidents from recurring. (Please see the Appendix for a sample Change Analysis form.)

REVIEW QUESTIONS

1. For what types of accidents is change analysis most useful?

2. What are the three types of accident-free situations that may be compared to an accident situation?

3. What steps are required to complete a thorough change analysis?

CHAPTER 8

Barrier Analysis

One of the most important purposes of a safety program is to identify hazards and establish barriers that will keep hazards from coming in contact with workers. Barrier analysis is the identification and analysis of barriers that are associated with accidents.

There are several types of barrier analysis. Most accident investigators use *hazard-barrier-target (HBT)* analysis, which considers potential hazards and potential targets and assesses the adequacy of barriers or other safeguards that should have prevented or mitigated the accident (Spear 2002). *Energy trace and barrier analysis (ETBA)* and *barrier and control analysis (BCA)* are useful for preventive analysis. ETBA traces the energy flow or energy path throughout the system and analyzes barriers for adequacy (Stephenson 1991). BCA locates hazards in a system and focuses on how to control them.

About Barrier Analysis

Barrier analysis for accident investigations can be traced back to the MORT system created by Bill Johnson for the Department of Energy. The technique was developed to look at an unwanted energy flow and determine what barriers could contain the flow. Safety professionals and accident investigators soon realized that the MORT system and barrier analysis could be used for reactive analyses such as accident investigations with excellent results (SSDC 1985).

Other types of barrier analyses and worksheets were used in the 1970s and 1980s and were called by different names. HBT analysis is the barrier analysis technique for accident investigations. It can be used for simple accidents as well as complex accidents to determine how the hazard reached the target.

The Barrier Analysis Approach

Two products of barrier analysis—a *chart* and an *analysis worksheet*—are used together to graphically explain accidents and analyze the barriers that need to be corrected or added. The chart illustrates hazards, barriers, and targets. The concept of the chart is simple: the investigator identifies a hazard and a target and then determines the barriers that could keep the hazard from reaching the target (see Exhibit 8.1). The analysis worksheet is used to describe the purpose and evaluate the performance of each barrier.

Exhibit 8.1

BARRIER ANALYSIS GRAPHICAL APPROACH

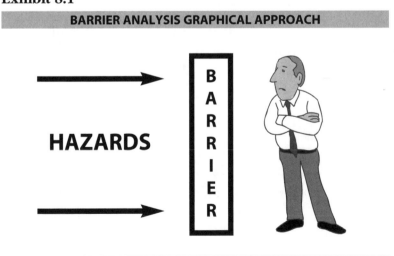

HAZARDS

B
A
R
R
I
E
R

The Barrier Analysis Process

The Barrier Analysis Chart

The first step in barrier analysis is to identify the hazard and the target. In the case of an electrocuted employee, for example, the hazard would be the electricity and the target would be the employee. The next step is to identify or brainstorm three categories of barriers— *barriers that failed, barriers that were not used,* and *barriers that did not exist* (see Exhibit 8.2).

The "analysis" part of barrier analysis can be completed only if all barriers associated with the accident are included. Brainstorming is a good way to make a comprehensive list of barriers (see Exhibit 8.3).

Many safety professionals and accident investigators categorize the types of barriers in another way as well—as *hard* (engineered) barriers and *soft* (administrative) barriers (System Safety Society 1997). Engineered barriers are physical restraints such as machine guards and protective equipment. Administrative barriers are policies and procedures—approved work methods, job training, and supervisory control (SSDC 1985). Exhibit 8.4 lists these types of barriers. Any barrier that would have prevented an accident must be incorporated into barrier analysis. Categorizing barriers as "hard" and "soft" is a good way to structure the brainstormed list of barriers.

The short example on the next page demonstrates the barrier analysis approach.

Exhibit 8.2

BARRIER CATEGORIES	
1. Barriers that failed	The barrier was in place and operational at the time of the accident, but it failed to prevent the accident.
2. Barriers that were not used	The barrier was available, but workers chose not to use it.
3. Barriers that did not exist	The barrier did not exist at the time of the accident.

Exhibit 8.3

BRAINSTORMING BARRIERS

Barriers that failed

1.
2.   *Brainstorm the barriers that were used that failed and record them here.*
3.

*Note: The key to this brainstorming session is to try to find **all** of the failed, unused, or nonexistent barriers. Do not be concerned if you are not certain which category they belong in.*

Barriers that were not used

1.
2.   *Brainstorm the barriers that were not used and record them here.*
3.

Barriers that did not exist

1.
2.   *Brainstorm the barriers that did not exist and record them here.*
3.

Note: The difference between these two categories is that "barriers not used" were available but were not used; "barriers that did not exist" were not available.

A worker was mowing a lawn when a rock flew out from beneath the mower and hit another worker who was walking to her car. In this example, a *failed* barrier is the plastic rock guard under the mower (an engineered barrier). A barrier *not used* is the company procedure that states that workers should stop mowing when people are walking nearby (an administrative barrier). A barrier that *did not exist* is a checklist/walkaround (an administrative barrier) the worker should use before mowing to check for rocks and hazards on the ground and check that all guards and equipment are in place, in good condition, and operating.

You will not find all categories and types of barriers in every investigation. However, it is critical to brainstorm all of the types and categories. As you can see in the lawn mower example, there were at least three ways this accident could have been prevented. A

Exhibit 8.4

TYPES OF BARRIERS	

	ENGINEERED	ADMINISTRATIVE	
H	1. Machine guards	1. Procedures	**S**
A	2. Personal protective equipment	2. Training	**O**
		3. Supervision	
R	3. Fall protection	4. Communication	**F**
	4. Interlocks	5. Work planning	
D	5. Electrical systems	6. Standards and regulations	**T**
	6. Safety valves		

barrier analysis summary chart is shown in Exhibit 8.5. This type of chart is useful not only for fact finding and analysis, but also for identifying corrective actions. Use the chart and the last column of the analysis form to prevent recurrence of an accident.

Exhibit 8.5

BARRIER ANALYSIS SUMMARY

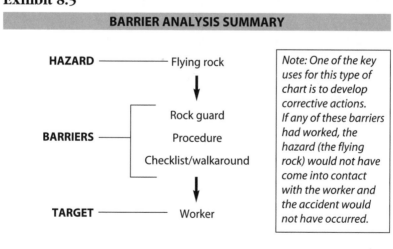

HAZARD ——————— Flying rock

BARRIERS —————
- Rock guard
- Procedure
- Checklist/walkaround

TARGET ——————— Worker

Note: One of the key uses for this type of chart is to develop corrective actions. If any of these barriers had worked, the hazard (the flying rock) would not have come into contact with the worker and the accident would not have occurred.

After all barriers are brainstormed, categorizing them can be handled in any way that benefits the organization. It is usually useful to separate engineered barriers from administrative barriers for ease in developing corrective actions to address or alleviate the problems. Engineered barriers that fail are usually design problems that can be corrected by engineers or the maintenance department, while administrative barriers that fail are usually management system problems that must be corrected by management.

The Barrier Analysis Worksheet

A worksheet is used to analyze the performance of the barriers. Exhibit 8.6 is a sample worksheet.

- **Column 1:** List the barriers, as illustrated in Exhibit 8.6. They can be listed by category (failed, not used, did not exist) or type (engineered or administrative).

- **Column 2:** Describe the intended function of each barrier. In the lawn mower example, the guard is an engineered barrier intended to keep items from flying out from under the mower deck. The procedure of stopping when someone is walking nearby is an administrative barrier that would have prevented a rock from hitting someone.

- **Column 3:** Evaluate the performance of the barrier. Each barrier is supposed to prevent a hazard from reaching a target. The lawn mower guard failed because it was defective, which allowed the rock to fly out.

Barrier Analysis Summary Chart

A barrier analysis summary chart is simply a list of the barriers associated with the accident. The list can be generated from the completed worksheet. This chart is an excellent addition to an accident report or management briefing, and it can also be used to develop corrective actions regarding the use of barriers.

Exhibit 8.6

BARRIER ANALYSIS FORM		
BARRIER	**PURPOSE OF BARRIER**	**PERFORMANCE OF BARRIER**
1.	1.	1.
2.	2.	2.
.	.	.
.	.	.
List all barriers.	Record the purpose of each barrier.	Analyze the performance of each barrier. Try to focus on the effect of the barrier on the accident or accident sequence.

Example Scenario

Barrier analysis analyzes barriers that failed, were not used, or did not exist. Most of the barriers in the forklift-ladder scenario either failed—supervisor training—or were not used—scheduling, a safety review, procedures, barricades, and communication. The barrier analysis form and barrier analysis summary chart are illustrated in Exhibit 8.7 and Exhibit 8.8 respectively. Barrier analysis demonstrates that when this accident occurred, many barriers existed that could have prevented the accident, but they were not used.

Exhibit 8.7

BARRIER ANALYSIS OF EXAMPLE SCENARIO

BARRIER	PURPOSE OF BARRIER	PERFORMANCE OF BARRIER
1. Scheduling and safety review	1. To evaluate all jobs and incorporate safety measures to ensure the safety of workers.	1. This barrier failed because a safety review was not performed for this task; performing it would have prompted the worker to use the correct procedure.
2. Job procedures	2. To ensure that all personnel who perform tasks are trained and use the same sequence.	2. This barrier failed because upper management did not enforce procedures and the new supervisor did not use the proper procedure.
3. Barricade	3. To warn forklift drivers that work is being done in the aisles.	3. This barrier failed because the warehouse supervisor failed to barricade the aisle.
4. Communication	4. To ensure that all information is shared between supervisors and employees.	4. This barrier failed because there was no communication about the job between the supervisors.
5. Supervisor training	5. To ensure that supervisors are adequately trained on management responsibilities.	5. This barrier failed because the new supervisor did not adequately perform his supervisory duties. The culture from upper management seems to be "Get the job done."

Exhibit 8.8

BARRIER ANALYSIS SUMMARY OF EXAMPLE SCENARIO

HAZARD ———— Hit by forklift/
Fall from height

BARRIERS ———
Review
Procedure
Barricade
Communication
Supervisor training

TARGET ———— Worker

Summary

Although many types of barrier analysis exist, all seek to accomplish the same goal—accident analysis. The hazard-barrier-target (HBT) type of barrier analysis can be used on all accidents regardless of size. It is a very efficient way to analyze smaller, first-aid-type accidents.

In accident investigations, barriers are either engineered or administrative. They can be viewed as barriers that failed, were not used, or did not exist. Barrier analysis helps an investigator to identify barriers, describe their purpose, and analyze their performance. After this analysis is performed, it can be used to develop corrective actions. (Please see the Appendix for a sample Barrier Analysis form.)

REVIEW QUESTIONS

1. What does barrier analysis try to accomplish?

2. How can barrier analysis be used to prevent accidents?

3. What three categories should be brainstormed during barrier analysis?

4. List two types of engineered barriers and two types of administrative barriers.

5. How can a barrier analysis summary be used to recommend corrective actions?

6. Many barriers are used when mowing, edging, and weed trimming. List all of the barriers that keep you from receiving an injury when doing yard work. Also, list any additional barriers that could be added or used that could prevent injuries from yard work.

CHAPTER 9

Tree Analysis
Fault Trees and Analytic Trees

In tree analysis, investigators use a graphic display of information to deductively analyze a human, equipment, or environmental system and determine paths to failure or success. Tree analysis identifies the interrelationships that led to the accident and helps to develop causal factors (Department of Energy 1999). Trees have been used in industry and government for many years in many different capacities. Two basic types of trees are used for accident investigations—*fault trees* and *analytic (developed) trees*. Fault trees show the actual events of the accident, and they grow as events leading up to the accident are discovered. Analytic trees are used to compare the accident situation to a tree developed before the accident happened—usually one based on an ideal situation. Examples of analytic trees include Management Oversight and Risk Tree (MORT), Project Evaluation Tree (PET), and system flowcharts.

Trees can be used in a variety of ways—as planning tools, in accident investigation analysis, in causal analysis, in project evaluation, and in quantitative analysis. In all of these applications, trees use deductive reasoning—they start with a general "top" event and

Exhibit 9.1

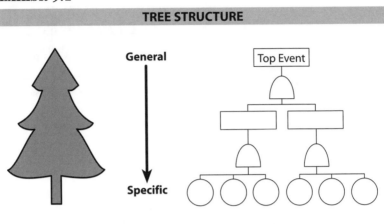

TREE STRUCTURE

continue down to specific causes. (Stephenson 1991). Exhibit 9.1 illustrates the tree structure.

About Tree Analysis

Three categories of trees are used to analyze various types of problems:

- fault (negative) trees
- positive trees
- analytic (developed) trees.

These categories are illustrated in Exhibit 9.2.

Fault (Negative) Trees

Fault tree analysis was developed for the U.S. Air Force in 1962. Fault trees are used qualitatively to determine failures in a system and quantitatively to determine failure rates. They are generally used to troubleshoot systems, for hazard (risk) analysis, and for accident investigations (Stephenson 1991).

Exhibit 9.2

THREE CATEGORIES OF ANALYTICAL TREES

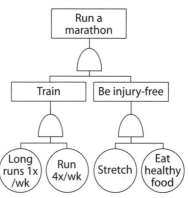

FAULT TREE

Manual alarm clock fails

Faulty clock | Forgot to wind | Forgot to set

This is a classic fault tree. A manual alarm clock could fail in three ways—the clock is faulty, the owner forgot to wind it, or the owner forgot to set it. If any one of these faults occurs, the clock will fail.

POSITIVE TREE

Run a marathon

Train | Be injury-free

Long runs 1x /wk | Run 4x/wk | Stretch | Eat healthy food

This example of a positive tree shows that in order for an average person to run a marathon, he or she must train and be injury-free. Training means running long and short runs each week; staying injury-free means stretching and eating healthy food.

ANALYTIC TREE (MORT)

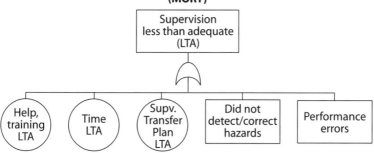

Supervision less than adequate (LTA)

Help, training LTA | Time LTA | Supv. Transfer Plan LTA | Did not detect/correct hazards | Performance errors

This is an example of a portion of a topic for "supervision less than adequate" (LTA). Questions are asked to determine whether each circle or rectangle is LTA. For each rectangle, more questions are asked.

Positive Trees

Positive trees display a system graphically—from general information to specific information. Creating an positive tree is a useful way to map systems components or provide information with a quick graphic. Positive trees can be developed early in the planning and design stages of a system, before an accident occurs, and then used as analytic trees if and when a failure or accident occurs later by comparing the failure or accident to the planned tree (Stephenson 1991).

Analytic (Developed) Trees

MORT, PET, and systems flowcharts are examples of analytic trees.

MORT is a safety system approach developed by Bill Johnson for the Department of Energy in the 1970s and used extensively in the 1970s and 1980s. It was developed as a proactive system safety tool and was later used for accident investigation. While it is still a viable accident investigation analysis tool, there is a shortage of individuals who know how to use it properly. It is an excellent tool to use after other analysis techniques have been completed to verify that all areas have been properly investigated (Johnson 1973).

PET was developed in 1988 by the U.S. Air Force as a structured tree approach that was simpler to learn and use than MORT (Stephenson 1991).

Other types of structured trees, such as *systems flowcharts,* can be used to show a system's structure graphically. For accident investigations, an investigator uses the tree to trace back through the system and find faults.

The Fault Tree Approach

The first step in constructing a fault tree is to determine the top event. For accident investigations, the top event is the accident, injury, or damage that occurred (Hammer 1993). Events that had to happen in order for the accident to happen are listed on the next tier of the tree.

Causal factors—fixable situations or correctable areas—are on the bottom tier of the tree. The corrective actions the accident investigator recommends will be geared to fixing these problems.

Symbols and gates are part of the fault-tree diagram. The most common tree symbols and gates are illustrated in Exhibit 9.3. Since the purpose of this chapter is to describe how trees can be used in accident investigations to determine causal factors, fault tree analysis methodologies and symbols that do not apply to accident investigation are not discussed.

Top events are "intermediate" events in fault-tree terminology. Failures and successes are logically diagramed under intermediate events. Under each intermediate event there may be other intermediate events (intermediate events may continue to be discovered as the investigation goes on), basic events (causal factors that stop the chain), undeveloped events (events that are inconsequential or about which not enough is known to continue the tree), or external events (events that are normally expected to occur). For example, if an employee stepped in a hole and broke his leg, the broken leg is the top event. The tree's next tier of events includes the intermediate events "hole not guarded" and "employee not paying attention." Going a step farther leads to basic events—the answers to questions like "Why was the employee not paying attention? Why was the hole not guarded?" The investigator must analyze all of the accident scenarios in order to structure an accurate, fully developed analytical tree.

All events in a fault tree are logically directed through gates (see Exhibit 9.3). An "and" gate means that all outputs must occur. For example, if the top event is sending an e-mail, then to make that top event occur, the computer must be turned on AND it must be connected to a phone line. Other things may have to happen as well, but both of these must definitely occur. An "or" gate means that if any one of the events on the second tier happens, the top event will happen. For example, if the top event is making a million dollars, then to make it occur you could be a professional athlete OR win the lottery.

Exhibit 9.3

COMMON TREE SYMBOLS

PRIMARY EVENT SYMBOLS

Basic event: A basic initiating fault requiring no further development

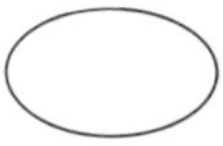

Conditioning event: Specific conditions or restrictions that apply to any logic gate

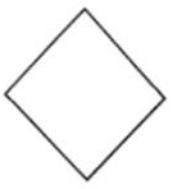

Undeveloped event: An event not further developed because it is either of insufficient consequence or information is unavailable

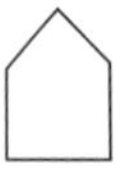

External event: An event normally expected to occur

INTERMEDIATE EVENT SYMBOLS

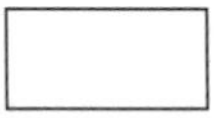

Intermediate event: A fault event that occurs because of one or more antecedent causes acting through logic gates

GATE SYMBOLS

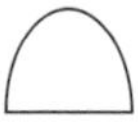

And: Output fault occurs if all the input faults occur

Or: Output fault occurs if at least one of the input faults occurs

TRANSFER SYMBOLS

Transfer in: Indicates the tree is developed further at each occurrence of the corresponding Transfer out (e.g., on another page)

Transfer out: Indicates that this portion of the tree must be attached at the corresponding Transfer in

Adapted from System Safety Society 1997

Once you determine the top event, the next step is to start tree construction. The tree construction steps for an accident are:

1. **Define the top event** (accident, injury, or damage).

2. **Investigate the accident.** (Learn about the system, the management structure, the accident, etc.)

3. **Construct the tree.** (Work from the top down asking why the top event occurred.)

4. **Develop causal factors.** (The basic events—the bottom tier of the tree—are causal factors.)

5. **Validate the tree.** (Ensure that all information has been analyzed.)

6. **Develop corrective actions.** (The basic events will make corrective actions apparent.)

The most important part of tree development is to understand the accident. If you do not have technical information, knowledge of the management structure, and facts about the accident sequence, your tree will be incomplete and possibly incorrect.

Fault Tree Process

To use fault tree analysis to investigate an accident:

1. **Start with the top event** (accident, injury, or damage).

2. **Determine the events necessary to produce the top event and the corresponding logic gates.**

3. **Continue until you reach correctable events** (basic events).

The general idea is to continue the tree until you reach a point at which there are no more events. Three types of events that can end a tree path are a *basic event* (a causal factor or fixable situation), an *undeveloped* event (one that is not applicable to the top event or about which not enough is known to evaluate it), or an *external* event (an event that is normally expected to occur). The process of diagraming the accident from general events to specific events using

Exhibit 9.4

DEDUCTIVE APPROACH

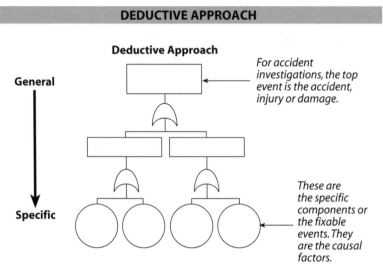

Deductive Approach

General

For accident investigations, the top event is the accident, injury or damage.

Specific

These are the specific components or the fixable events. They are the causal factors.

logic gates will help you to develop the causal factors of the accident. The process of tree development is illustrated in Exhibit 9.4.

Developing a fault tree for even a small accident is a practical and easy way to portray the accident. A short example of a fisherman failing to catch fish was used in Chapter 7 to demonstrate change analysis. Here's how the same scenario can be used to demonstrate fault tree analysis:

Bob had gone fishing every day for the last twenty years to catch his lunch and dinner for the day. One day, he did not catch any fish. Susan decided to use an analytical tree to find out why Bob did not catch any fish that day. The top event was failure to catch fish. The second tier of events in the fault tree included events that would keep Bob from catching fish. Susan found out that in order to catch fish, one must have the right bait, use the correct hook size, and be where the fish are. Starting with this knowledge, she asked, "Why didn't Bob have the right bait?

Exhibit 9.5

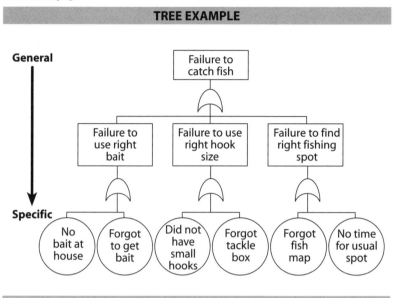

Why didn't Bob have the correct size hook? Why didn't Bob fish in his usual place? " in order to find basic events (the bottom tier of the tree) that could ultimately cause failure of the top event (see Exhibit 9.5).

The key to this type of analysis is to ask "Why?" at each event in the tree to try to discover causal factors.

The Analytic Tree Approach

The analytic tree approach to analyzing an accident is more proactive than other techniques because the tree is predefined—developed before an accident occurs. If an accident does occur, the accident sequence is compared to the sequence of the previously defined tree to uncover failures or faults that will help the investigator to discover causal factors.

Management Oversight and Risk Tree (MORT)

MORT is probably the best-known analytic tree technique. It was the first engineering and safety tool used to merge safety management and safety engineering (Bahr 1997). MORT was an excellent attempt at a systematic approach for analyzing the adequacy of programs, procedures, controls, policies, and management systems (Vincoli 1994). It is still a viable technique for accident investigation, but the number of trained individuals and MORT proponents is rapidly decreasing.

The *MORT User's Manual* describes MORT as

> ". . . a logic diagram in the form of a 'work sheet' that illustrates a long series of interrelated questions. MORT is a comprehensive analytical procedure that provides a disciplined method for determining the causes and contributing factors of major accidents. Alternatively, it serves as a tool to evaluate the quality of an existing system. While similar in many respects to fault tree analysis, MORT is more generalized and presents over 1,500 specific elements of an ideal 'universal' management program for optimizing environmental, safety and health, and other programs" (SSDC 1992, iii).

Accident investigators who use MORT work through the tree by asking questions listed in the *MORT User's Manual*. Each question is given a response that is marked in color on the MORT chart. The possible responses to the questions are:

1. Less than adequate (LTA) (red)

2. Adequate (green)

3. Need more information (blue)

4. Not applicable (black)

A complete tree contains ninety-eight generic events (problems) and more than fifteen hundred basic events. Using MORT can be extremely confusing—it is easy to get lost in the chart. MORT is also not suited for some smaller accidents, but the biggest problem with the technique is that it assumes there is an ideal system (Bahr 1997). A small example of the MORT process and its corresponding set of questions is illustrated in Exhibit 9.6. The investigator asks the questions, answers according to the facts of the accident, and marks the tree with the appropriate color coding. As the tree is developed, the investigator continues to explore paths indicated by red ("less than adequate") marks to learn why the system failed.

PET and Systems Flow Charts

PET and systems flow charts work on the same principles as MORT. A tree developed before an accident is used to find possible faults or errors in the system. There are many types of predefined trees, and many companies have developed their own management system trees.

The Analytic Tree Process
(Using MORT for Validation)

It is probably better to use MORT as a method of validating another type of investigation technique than to use it as your primary technique. It can help to ensure that you did not miss an area that should have been investigated and that the proper causal factors were determined. If you consult the MORT chart and find that some areas were missed, the investigation can continue. If your investigation has been thorough, it will not take you long to complete the MORT chart.

Example Scenario

Once again using the forklift-ladder accident, part of a tree that could be used to analyze this accident is illustrated in Exhibit 9.7. The top event is the warehouse supervisor falling off the ladder. The next level is the forklift hitting the ladder, and the next is three ways that a forklift could hit a ladder. The investigator asks questions about these three reasons to arrive at the bottom tier—basic events or causal

Exhibit 9.6

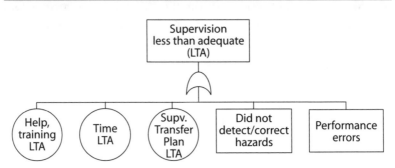

ANALYTIC TREE (MORT)

Once you decided that supervision was a problem, these questions would be asked:

- **Supervision LTA:** Was the worksite supervision adequate? Were the necessary supportive services adequate? If the answers were no, then you would continue further on the chart (tree).

- **Help and training LTA:** Were the help and assistance given to supervisors adequate to enable them to fulfill their roles? Was the feedback of information to the supervisor adequate? Was it furnished in a form usable by the supervisor? What training had the supervisor been given in general supervision? What training had the supervisor been given in safety? Has the supervisor training program been evaluated?

- **Time LTA:** Did the supervisor have sufficient time to thoroughly examine the job?

- **Supervisor transfer plan LTA:** Were there any gaps or overlaps in the supervisory assignments related to the event? If the supervisor was recently transferred to the job, was there protocol for orderly transfer of safety information from the old to the new supervisor?

- **Did not detect/correct hazards:** When did the supervisor last make an inspection of the area? Was any unsafe condition present in this accident/incident also present at the time of inspection? Was the condition detected?

- **Performance errors:** Was the work activity at the worksite free of performance errors by work level personnel?

SSDC 1992

factors: "Why did the warehouse supervisor not communicate what he was about to do to the supervisor of the night shift? Was his failure to communicate a training issue, or did he just decide to disregard the procedures? Why was the forklift traveling with an obstructed view?" If the accident investigator does not know the answers to these questions, he or she must interview witnesses, obtain documents, or perform tests to find the answers.

Exhibit 9.7

ANALYTIC TREE PROCESS FOR SCENARIO EXAMPLE

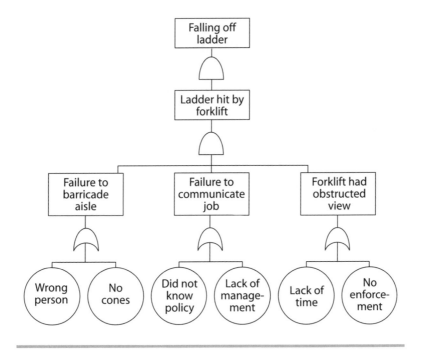

Summary

Many techniques are used in tree analysis. Each technique works better for some types of investigation than for others, and some techniques are inappropriate for some types of investigations. The major benefit of using tree analysis is that trees are, for the most part, structured, easy to create, and easy to understand. You will be able to use one or more of these techniques to investigate almost every accident you encounter. (Please see the Appendix for a sample Analytical Tree Flowchart.)

REVIEW QUESTIONS

1. Which type of gate requires that all outputs must occur?

2. What are the three categories of tree analysis? Briefly describe each.

3. What is MORT?

4. What are the steps of tree construction?

5. Continue the analytic tree process for the example scenario (Exhibit 9.7).

CHAPTER 10

Specialized and Computerized Techniques

So far this book has discussed four major types of analytical techniques: events and causal factors analysis, change analysis, barrier analysis, and tree analysis. Many other specialized analytical techniques can be used in accident investigations, and each has a role in certain situations. (NOTE: In some types of accidents, these specialized techniques may yield so much information and so many possible causes that the investigator cannot deal with them. The process becomes too confusing and frustrating. The investigator must learn to use the appropriate technique for each type of accident.)

Some of the newest analytical techniques for accident investigation involve the use of computers and software. Some programs simply allow investigators to portray accidents graphically, but others actually help to analyze accidents. Computerized techniques range from computerized trees to fully animated accident reconstruction programs.

Specialized Techniques

Time Loss Analysis

Time loss analysis was developed for the National Transportation Safety Board. It is a graphical analysis tool that investigators can use proactively to understand, develop, and evaluate interventions and emergency response actions, and reactively to give credit to good emergency response efforts or interventions in accident situations.

Time loss analysis helps the investigator to evaluate how the timing of emergency response or loss control actions affected the loss caused by the accident and to analyze the losses that occurred as the events leading up to the accident progressed. It is useful in determining how loss control interventions changed (or could have changed) the amount of loss and how time increased or decreased losses or costs. It provides a way to analyze the interventions in an accident situation and determine how they changed the course of the accident sequence (SSDC 1987).

To use this technique, investigators follow these steps:

- **Discover and analyze all interventions that took place leading up to and during the accident.**

- **Determine whether these interventions increased, decreased, or had no effect on the outcome (the accident sequence).** For example, in a car crash with an injury, what is the effect of the vehicle having anti-lock brakes? Do the brakes allow the car to stop any sooner or in a shorter distance? What about airbags? What about crumple zones?

- **Assign a time value to each intervention.** The time value can be an actual number or a relative position on the chart. For example, the brakes start to act as soon as the driver senses danger and applies them. The anti-lock brake mechanism activates when the wheels begin to lock. The air bags activate at the moment of impact. The crumple zones crumple after the initial impact as the car continues to move, increasing the damage to the car but distributing energy away from the passengers.

- **Evaluate the loss.** The loss axis is usually marked in dollars or units of loss (amount of water flooded or gas leaked, number of people injured, number of vehicles damaged).

Exhibit 10.1 illustrates a time loss analysis chart for the simple car crash described above. The lowest amount of loss occurs if all three interventions—the anti-lock brakes, air bags, and crumple zones—are used. Even if all three are used, there will be some damage; however, if they are not used, the amount of loss will be much greater.

Human Factors Analysis

There are many methods of human factors analysis, and a human factors or ergonomics expert should perform the analyses. The basis of human factors analysis is to identify human/machine/environment interaction and to determine whether the interaction had an effect on

Exhibit 10.1

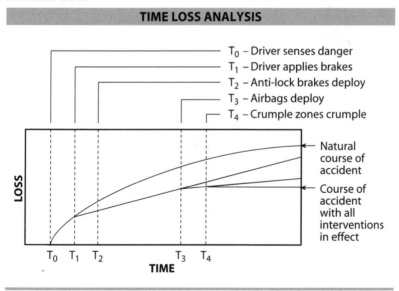

TIME LOSS ANALYSIS

T_0 – Driver senses danger
T_1 – Driver applies brakes
T_2 – Anti-lock brakes deploy
T_3 – Airbags deploy
T_4 – Crumple zones crumple

Natural course of accident

Course of accident with all interventions in effect

LOSS

T_0 T_1 T_2 T_3 T_4

TIME

the accident. There is some type of human involvement in all aspects of an accident. The key is to determine the human involvement and the human capabilities to perform the task.

To conduct a human/machine/environment analysis of an accident, the expert follows these steps:

- **Analyze how the human interacted with the machine, equipment, environment, etc.**

- **List the bad interactions in the accident sequence.** These are the interactions that do not favor the capabilities of the human body. Human capabilities include physical interactions (strength, flexibility, range of motion, eyesight, hearing), mental interactions (knowledge, intelligence, training), and emotional interactions (morale, motivation, attitude).

Other types of human factors analysis analyze anthropometry, biomechanics, work physiology, selection and training of personnel, job tasks, and workloads. In this type of analysis, the focus is on the work environment that produces bad behavior. The safety professional tries to eliminate the bad behavior instead of focusing on human error (Oakley and Smith 2000).

Integrated Accident Event Matrix

An integrated accident event matrix includes a list of all individuals who were at the scene of an accident and a time-based chart that shows their interactions (DOE 1999). This matrix allows an investigator to analyze what each individual was doing at the time of the accident. Although the chart can include any amount of time before the accident, it usually only covers the ten to twenty minutes before the accident occurred. This type of matrix is helpful for many types of accident investigations and is very simple to perform. It is a low-tech method of accident reconstruction.

To perform an integrated accident event matrix, the investigator follows these steps:

- List all of the individuals who may have been involved in the accident in the left column of the matrix.

- Mark the next columns with times, and write each person's activities under the appropriate time. Exhibit 10.2 illustrates an example of an integrated accident event matrix. It shows that there was no interaction between the pipefitter and the mechanic and that the supervisor yelled at the pipefitter to get the job done as soon as possible, interrupting him. Creating an integrated accident event matrix is a simple technique that can be used to discover interactions between people.

Exhibit 10.2

INTEGRATED ACCIDENT EVENT MATRIX				
Note: This technique is very helpful in fatal accidents or other situations where some viewpoints are not available.				
PEOPLE	**10:01**	**10:02**	**10:03**	**10:04**
List all people who could give information about inter-actions and help to analyze what occurred at the time of the accident.	*Record what each worker was doing at each time in the sequence.*			
Pipefitter	Walked to job site	Turned to talk with super-visor	Went to electrical box and turned on breaker	Walked to equipment; found mechanic in pain
Supervisor	Talked with vendor	Yelled at pipefitter	Finished paperwork for pipefitter	Finished paperwork
Mechanic	Worked on equipment	Worked on equipment	Talked on cell phone	Received electrical shock

Failure Modes and Effects Analysis

Failure modes and effects analysis is usually used as a proactive safety tool to help safety professionals analyze how failures can affect systems. The technique can also be used reactively for accident investigations and is especially useful if the accident was caused by a system failure. In accident investigations, all failure modes should be analyzed to determine whether they caused the accident. While all failures are important, only the one(s) that probably caused the accident is included in the accident sequence.

To use failure modes and effects analysis to analyze a system, the investigator follows these steps:

- List all of the major assemblies of a system and then list all of its components. (Of course, before doing this, it is important for everyone involved in the investigation to understand the system and all of its components [Hammer 1993].) For example, a coffee maker has two *assemblies:* a pot and a filtering system. The *components* of a simple coffee machine are a power cord, a heating element, a water containment area, a filter and coffee area, and a pot.

- Brainstorm a list of all possible failure modes for each component. For each one, ask, "How could this fail?" There may be more than one way for a component to fail.

- Evaluate each failure mode (Stephenson 1990). Ask, "If a system or component failed in this way, how would the system be affected?"

If this technique is used for an accident investigation, the investigator should find all of the modes of failure that could produce the accident situation. Failure modes and effects analysis is useful in determining corrective actions—how to prevent the failure mode.

Design Criteria Analysis

Design criteria analysis is one component of change analysis (see Chapter 7). Using this technique, the safety professional tries to discover the ideal way to perform a task. During design criteria analysis, the investigator identifies the codes, design requirements,

Exhibit 10.3

FAILURE MODES AND EFFECTS ANALYSIS FORM			
COMPONENTS	**FAILURE MODES**	**EFFECTS OF FAILURE ON THE SYSTEM**	**EFFECTS OF FAILURE ON ACCIDENT SEQUENCE**
1.	1. a.	1. a.	1.
	b.	b.	
	c.	c.	
2.	2. a.	2. a.	2.
	b.	b.	
	c.	c.	
List each component of each assembly involved in the accident.	*For each component, brainstorm all the ways the component could fail.*	*For each failure mode, answer the question "If the component failed in this way, how would the system be affected?"*	*In an accident investigation, list the effects of failure modes on the accident sequence.*

procedures, and policies that should be followed when performing a task and describes how to comply with all of these standards (DOE 1999). In accident investigations, all standards that pertain to the task that was being performed when the accident happened are identified. They will help the investigator to structure a safe and appropriate way to perform the task, and this way will be compared to how the task was being performed when the accident occurred.

Performing a design criteria analysis is a fairly simple process:

- Review all codes, design requirements, procedures, and policies to determine how to perform the task correctly.

- Compare these standards to how the task was actually being performed when the accident took place.

This technique is useful because once the investigator defines the correct, safe way to perform a task, it will be easy to determine corrective actions that will prevent future accidents.

Other Specialized Techniques

Expert Techniques

Some techniques that can be useful in accident investigation are best performed by experts. Examples include:

- *Software hazard analysis.* Helps investigators to analyze software failures and find causal factors in computer systems.

- *Common cause failure analysis.* Used to find system failures that led to accidents.

- *Sneak circuit analysis.* Looks at sneaks (failures) in a system or circuit.

Failure Analysis and Structural Analysis

Failure analysis and structural analysis can be used for accident investigations to determine types of failures and structural flaws that led to an accident.

Scientific Modeling

Many types of modeling can be used to describe possible accident scenarios or to sample data to reconstruct scenarios. These types of analysis are performed by experts who understand data collection and analysis processes. Most of these types of analysis are performed in a laboratory setting.

Accident Reconstruction

Accident reconstructions may be simulated or computer-generated. To reconstruct an accident, the investigator finds out how each step in the accident sequence occurred. Once this sequence is determined, the reconstruction will help to analyze the effects or potential effects of the each event in the sequence.

Computerized Techniques

Graphical Programs

Investigators can use graphical programs such as Microsoft Visio™ and CorelDRAW™ to create events and causal factors charts, graph analytical trees, draw barrier analysis summary charts, and structure cause and effects diagrams. Presentation programs such as Microsoft PowerPoint™ and Corel Presentations™ can be used to draw simple charts and analytical trees. While these programs graphically display the results of the accident investigation, they do not actually analyze the investigation.

Analytical Programs

A new breed of computerized programs, however, *can* help accident investigators with problem solving, investigation, and analysis. These programs can be used not only to find causal factors and corrective actions, but also to turn the analyses into written reports.

Many custom programs have been designed for accident analysis, events and causal factors charting and analysis, and tree analysis. Using a computer program does not take the place of investigating, analyzing, and thinking, however. Four accident investigation and problem solving programs are:

- REASON® Root Cause Analysis by Decision Systems, Inc.

- Apollo Root Cause Analysis and RealityCharting™ by Apollo Associated Services

- TapRooT® System with SnapCharT® Software and Root Cause Tree® Software by System Improvements, Inc.

- RootCause LEADER™ Software by ABS Consulting, Inc.

The following short descriptions of the capabilities of each program were obtained from the companies' web sites. Web site addresses are listed in the bibliography at the end of the book.

REASON® Root Cause Analysis

The latest version of this root cause analysis software from Decision Systems, Inc. is called REASON® 5. REASON® believes root cause analysis should be a validated and consistent process that discovers the root cause of a problem so that business practices can be used to prevent recurrence of the problem. One of the key features of REASON® 5 is that it gives the user a "railroad track to get you to the correct root cause." In other words, it gives the user the tools to find the failure. The program leads the user to ask the right questions, and thus arrive at the end point (root cause).

This software is used not only for accident investigations, but for any type of problem solving or process improvement. A validation step is built into the software; this gives consistency to the root cause analysis process. REASON® 5 does not attempt to funnel the user into a select number of root causes.

Other important functions are a corrective action database that tracks corrective actions and a searchable query for searching previous accidents, issues, root causes, and corrective actions. The software also has a powerful report editor. This program can be used for both reactive and proactive situations. (Decision Systems Inc. 2003.)

Apollo Root Cause Analysis

When Apollo Associated Services first started out, it introduced an approach to basic problem solving that also works well for accident investigation. Apollo has developed a very effective training program and cause-and-effect process. The cause-and-effect process can be performed either on a computer or on paper. The process and a particular method of analysis is Apollo's real product. As the computer has grown to be a more important tool in accident investigation, Apollo has developed a variety of computerized charting programs. The newest is RealityCharting™.

RealityCharting™ is a graphical program that facilitates the cause-and-effect charting process. One of its features is the ability to drag and drop causes to any location on the chart. The software also has a validation step called the Rules Check feature that examines the chart for deviations from the rules for the cause-and-effect process. A solution tracking feature and a report generator are also included (Apollo Associated Services 2003).

TapRooT®

The TapRooT® System consists of two computerized accident investigation programs, SnapCharT® and Root Cause Tree®. These products are definitely an improvement over using adhesive notes to chart events and causal factors. SnapCharT® is a graphical program that draws charts and diagrams and allows easy modifications. The result is a presentation-quality chart.

The Root Cause Tree® software picks up where SnapCharT® leaves off. SnapCharT® determines what happened, and Root Cause Tree® finds root causes and develops corrective actions. This software features a Root Cause Tree® dictionary and a Corrective Action Helper® module. A built-in reporting feature and integrated databases ensure that corrective actions are tracked. (Systems Improvement Inc. 2003.)

RootCause LEADER™ Software

RootCause LEADER™ allows accident investigators to investigate and track any type of incident, event, or mishap. It can also perform data trending and analysis, generate report forms, and include a detailed background/description for each causal factor and root cause. This software can identify root causes of incidents, events, accidents, near misses, reliability problems, quality impacts, or business losses.

RootCause LEADER™ has five key features: identifying conse-quences, using Root Cause Map™, attaching photo files and other documents, tracking recommendations, and trending. The conse-quence categories and ABS's Root Cause Map™ are features for customizing the database and helping the investigator identify root causes. (ABS Consulting Inc. 2003.)

Summary

Many specialized and computerized analytical techniques can be used for accident investigation. In order to receive the most information from a technique, it must be performed in the correct situation. Many techniques must be performed only by an expert. Many system safety analyses can be used for accident analysis, but caution should be used to ensure that the data gained is useful. These analyses may identify an overwhelming amount of data that may not be practical for the accident investigation. The new computerized analysis and problem-solving programs are becoming increasingly important to investigators.

REVIEW QUESTIONS

1. What does time loss analysis try to analyze?

2. Which techniques must be performed by an expert?

3. What does a failure modes and effects analysis look for?

4. What is the difference between a design criteria analysis and change analysis?

5. How can computerized techniques be helpful in accident investigations?

Part IV

PREVENTING ACCIDENTS

Part IV focuses on how to prevent future accidents, which is the ultimate purpose of conducting accident investigations. Determining the accident sequence and the causal factors prepares the accident investigator to determine corrective actions that will prevent similar accidents. Corrective actions should be initiated, documented, and followed up (audited) to ensure that they are performing as intended.

Writing an accident report or filling out an accident form is not simply an exercise in paperwork. The report should document that the facts and analysis are correct, the accident sequence has been determined, and corrective actions have been developed to avoid recurrence of the accident.

Objectives for Part IV:

* Understand the purpose of corrective actions and be able to develop effective corrective actions and recommendations for accidents.
* Understand the relationships among facts, analysis, causes, and corrective actions.
* Be aware of the importance of documenting an accident.
* Understand the importance of follow-up activities for accidents and corrective actions to ensure completion and effectiveness.

CHAPTER 11

Recommending Corrective Actions

T he subject of this chapter seldom receives the attention it deserves. The purpose of an accident investigation is to prevent recurrence of the same accident or a similar accident and to correct problems in the safety program so that other types of accidents can be avoided. The important steps of any accident investigation are gathering evidence, discovering and analyzing the accident sequence, determining causal factors, and finding corrective actions that will prevent future accidents. The last three steps are linked to the steps before them: Once all of the facts are gathered and analyzed, the accident sequence is determined. Once the accident sequence is determined, causal factors become clear. And once the causal factors are established, corrective actions can be developed.

Causal Factors

A causal factor is an event or circumstance that helped to cause an accident. An investigator must examine causal factors at all levels— management, worker, engineering (design), and policy—in order to to provide corrective actions and accountability for those corrective actions. Use an events and causal factors chart to develop the causal factors, and ensure that none are missed. All possible causal factors should be listed, no matter how minor they seem, so that when corrective actions are developed, the investigator can be positive that all of the causal factors have been addressed.

Teaching a worker who has been involved in an accident to work more safely will probably prevent that worker from repeating the accident, but causal factors frequently go beyond the worker level. If the causal factor is a policy issue or a design issue, then the corrective action must be addressed at that level in order to avoid future accidents. An accident investigation is a chance to look at failures in the safety program and correct them. It is not a time to place blame or attribute human error, but to look at what caused the human error.

Corrective Actions

Although companies use different terms to describe fixing the problems that caused accidents, "recommendations" and "corrective actions" seem to be the most widely used. A corrective action, if implemented, should "fix" a causal factor—prevent it from causing another accident. Corrective actions can take the form of engineering redesigns, task redesigns, policy or procedure changes, and equipment changes, among others. Any action that can be taken to prevent future accidents is a corrective action, as shown in Exhibit 11.1.

To be effective in preventing future accidents, corrective actions should be implemented using the three-step process shown in Exhibit 11.2.

1. **Develop the corrective actions** after the investigation produces causal factors.

2. **Track the corrective actions.** A database is useful for organizing and tracking information about the corrective actions.

Exhibit 11.1

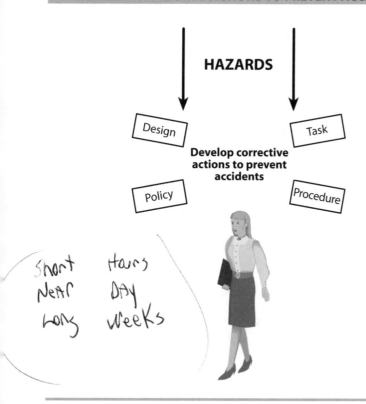

DEVELOP CORRECTIVE ACTIONS TO PREVENT ACCIDENTS

HAZARDS

Design

Task

Develop corrective actions to prevent accidents

Policy

Procedure

Short   Hours
Near   Day
Long   Weeks

---

3. **Follow up** to ensure that the corrective actions have been followed as initiated. If a corrective action is not used, accident prevention is not ensured.

Developing Corrective Actions

A corrective action should fix a problem and prevent accidents. All causal factors should have at least one corrective action (DOE 1999).

Tips for Developing Corrective Actions

Make

?

- Every accident should have at least one causal factor.
- Develop at least one corrective action for each causal factor.

Exhibit 11.2

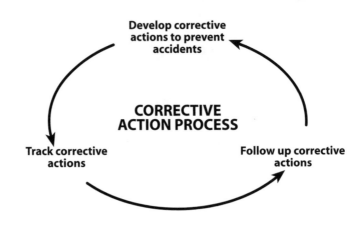

THREE-STEP PROCESS FOR CORRECTIVE ACTIONS

Develop corrective
actions to prevent
accidents

**CORRECTIVE
ACTION PROCESS**

Track corrective
actions

Follow up corrective
actions

- Communicate corrective actions clearly.

- Make causal factors and corrective actions very specific so that the worker, supervisor, or manager knows exactly what the problem is and how to fix it. "Human error" as a causal factor and "training" as the corresponding corrective action, for example, are too general to be of use. Examples of useful, specific corrective actions are "Design a metal guard that prevents contact with the blade"; "Provide electrical training for all maintenance workers, including lockout/tagout procedures"; and "Increase the corporate inspector's audit schedule to include warehouse activities." The more specifics included in the corrective action, the better the chance that accidents will be prevented.

Recommending Corrective Actions that Eliminate Hazards

There are usually several ways to fix a problem, and some ways are more likely to prevent accidents than others. Try to choose a corrective action that will eliminate a hazard when possible. Two types of hazard reduction strategies work well to develop corrective actions and fix problems—hazard control precedence, which is widely used and accepted in the safety area, and a strategy taken from epidemiology called *injury control.*

The hazard control precedence shows the order in which hazard control methods should be considered. At the top of the list is eliminating the hazard, a step that usually involves design or redesign. The next step is to design for minimum risk or, in some cases, substitute a less hazardous material. Next is to design in safety devices such as guards, although they do not reduce or eliminate the hazard but simply cover it up. Warning devices, personal protective equipment, procedures, and training also do not eliminate or reduce the hazard, so they are toward the bottom of the list. If none of the earlier steps works, the last choice is to accept the risk. Accepting the risk is usually not considered a corrective action and is not used in accident investigations (System Safety Society 1997). There has already been one accident and having another is not acceptable. Exhibit 11.3 outlines the hazard control precedence.

Exhibit 11.3

HAZARD CONTROL PRECEDENCE

PRIORITIES IN SEEKING A HAZARD CONTROL SOLUTION

1. Design to eliminate hazard conditions.

2. Design for minimum risk.

3. Design in safety devices.

4. Design separate warning devices.

5. Develop operating procedures (including protective clothing, equipment, and devices) and train personnel to use them.

6. Develop administrative rules.

7. Require management to accept risk.

"This precedence emphasizes building safety into the system and minimizing reliance on human input. Safety as part of the design makes it integral to the system" (System Safety Society 1997, 1–3).

The second hazard reduction strategy, based on epidemiology and injury control, was developed by William Haddon, Jr. (1970) and lists ten strategies for injury control:

1. *Prevent the creation of the hazard in the first place.* Example: Do not allow the manufacture of particularly hazardous vehicles such as motorcycles, minibikes, or all-terrain vehicles.

2. *Reduce the amount of the hazard brought into being.* Example: Allow the sale of handguns only to police and military units.

3. *Prevent the release of a hazard that already exists.* Example: Improve the braking power of motor vehicles.

4. *Modify the release or spatial distribution of release of the hazard from its source.* Example: Use child restraints and seat belts in motor vehicles.

5. *Separate, in time or space, the hazard and that which is to be protected.* Example: Remove roadside trees and poles.

6. *Separate the hazard and that which is to be protected by interposition of a material barrier.* Example: Install air bags in passenger vehicles.

7. *Modify basic relevant qualities of the hazard.* Example: Eliminate sharp points and edges on vehicle exteriors.

8. *Make what is to be protected more resistant to damage from the hazard.* Example: Require physical conditioning before participation in sports that produce conditioning-related injuries.

9. *Begin to counter the damage already done by the environmental hazard.* Example: Increase the use of smoke detectors and carbon monoxide detectors.

10. *Stabilize, repair, and rehabilitate the object of the damage.* Example: Provide prosthetic devices for amputees.

(Adapted from Haddon 1970)

Haddon's list is made up of basic injury control strategies as opposed to workplace hazard control strategies. The list provides a basic understanding of how to prevent injury. Find out more about injury control by reading Haddon (1970) and Robertson (1998).

Tracking Corrective Actions

Once a set of corrective actions has been developed, the actions must be implemented. It does no good to conduct an excellent accident investigation, find causal factors, and develop useful corrective actions if your company fails to implement the corrective actions or implements them very slowly. The best way to ensure that corrective actions are acted on is to track them.

- Responsibility
- Target Date
- Status

Tips for Tracking Corrective Actions

- Establish a timetable for each corrective action. If all the actions are assigned to a specific department or individual, they are usually implemented in a timely manner.

- Consider using a database to track corrective actions. Include fields for a description of the action, an anticipated completion date, and the party responsible for carrying out the action.

- Conduct a follow-up to make sure the corrective actions are in place and working correctly. This will be discussed further in Chapter 12.

Example Scenario

Exhibit 11.4 shows the completed events and causal factors analysis for the forklift-and-ladder accident. The causal factors found for this accident are lack of barricades; management's failure to plan, schedule, and communicate the job; the corporate culture of getting jobs done quickly (including upper management's lack of enforcement of policies and procedures); and failure to follow policies and procedures. The events and causal factors analysis, barrier analysis, and change analysis earlier in this book make it clear that this accident is more complicated

Exhibit 11.4

SCENARIO EVENTS AND CAUSAL FACTORS ANALYSIS

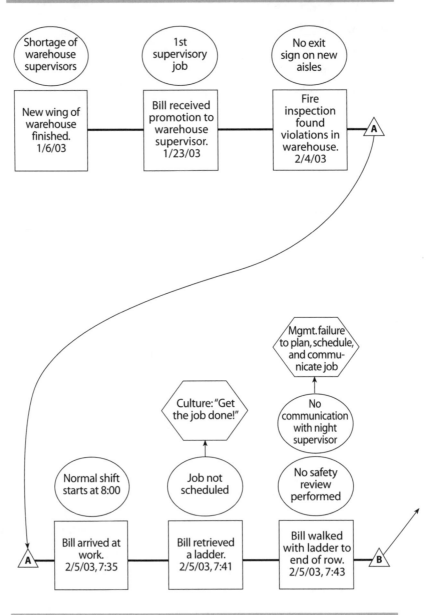

SCENARIO EVENTS AND CAUSAL FACTORS ANALYSIS, continued

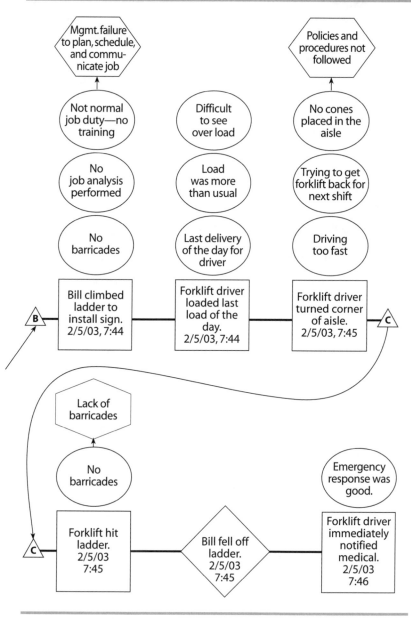

than just a "forgot to barricade" issue. If the accident investigator had analyzed only the barricade issue, many important prevention steps would have been missed. Exhibit 11.5 lists the causal factors and some corrective actions that may prevent recurrence of this accident. Try to find more causal factors and corrective actions that could prevent accidents like this.

The example scenario is an example of management and policy failure. Since the accident occurred while someone was performing a non-recurring job, engineering fixes are not appropriate, but there may be hazard elimination strategies that could be used. Can you think of any?

Exhibit 11.5

CAUSAL FACTORS AND CORRECTIVE ACTIONS FOR EXAMPLE SCENARIO

CAUSAL FACTORS	CORRECTIVE ACTIONS
1. Lack of barricades	1. Train workers and supervisors on how to barricade aisles.
2. Management failure to plan, schedule, and communicate job	2. Develop management policy and train management on planning, scheduling, and communicating jobs and tasks.
3. Corporate culture to get jobs done quickly (upper management's lack of enforcement of policies and procedures)	3. Develop an auditing system matrix for supervisors, managers, and corporate employees that includes enforcing policies and procedures.
4. Forklift policies and procedures not followed.	4. Train supervisors and forklift drivers on policies and procedures and develop enforcement audits.

Summary

Corrective actions—the actions that will prevent recurrence of the accident—are the backbone of the accident investigation. Corrective actions must be based on the causal factors, developed clearly and objectively, tracked until completion, and followed up to ensure that they are in place and working correctly. If a corrective action is not initiated, it cannot prevent accidents. Corrective actions should be developed at all levels of accountability and at the highest level of hazard control precedence possible to ensure that the hazard is controlled.

REVIEW QUESTIONS

1. What is a corrective action?

2. What is the relationship between a causal factor and a corrective action?

3. How must a corrective action be written?

4. List the hazard control precedence.

5. Why should a company track corrective actions?

6. For the example scenario, try to find more causal factors and corrective actions that will prevent accidents.

Reporting and Follow-up

Reporting and documentation are important parts of the accident investigation process. There are many reporting styles and methods, but whichever way is chosen, it is important to ensure consistency in the reports.

The last step in the accident investigation process is to follow up to ensure that the corrective actions have been initiated and are being followed. Many companies forget this important step. An accident will not recur if its causal factors are determined, corrective actions are developed, and the corrective actions are initiated and in place. A follow-up ensures this.

Reporting

The three types of accident investigation reports are listed in Exhibit 12.1. The first is a *log*—a medical log, accident log, or even the OSHA 300 log. The second is a *form* that has space to document facts, causal factors, and corrective actions. The third is a written accident investigation *report.* All three types should convey the facts of the investigation, the causal factors of the accident, and the corrective

These Q's

139

actions that will prevent future accidents. Near misses can be investigated and documented in the same manner as accidents, and this can be helpful in preventing accidents.

Accident Logs

Accident logs are simply lists of a company's accidents—injuries, property damage, and near misses. Medical departments usually keep a log of employees who visit the department. The safety department should at least keep logs of near misses, minor accidents, and minor property damage, but any accident, near miss, property damage, or injury can and probably should be investigated in addition to recording it in a log. Accident logs can be very comprehensive or very simple as illustrated in Exhibit 12.2.

Most companies are required to keep an OSHA 300 log. All recordable injuries, lost workday injuries, illnesses, and fatalities (as described by the OSHA Recordkeeping Standard) are recorded here. Keeping this log is required by law, but it is not a substitute for proper accident investigation, including development of causal factors and corrective actions. The log is an excellent tool for determining trends and possible points of weakness in the safety program.

Exhibit 12.1

REPORTING AND DOCUMENTATION

Accident Log—list of all accidents, injuries, and near misses.

Accident Form—form used to collect information about an accident, document the accident, and list the causal factors and corrective actions.

Accident Report—a document that includes the accident sequence, facts, analysis, causal factors, and corrective actions.

Exhibit 12.2

ACCIDENT LOG					
Date	Name	Injured Body Part	Accident Description	Causal Factors	Corrective Actions

Accident Forms

Accident forms collect two types of information:

- **Facts:** the date and time of the accident, the personnel involved, description of the accident, and other valuable information.

- **Analysis:** causal factors and corrective actions.

Some forms are very basic, while others can be many pages long and represent a fairly comprehensive investigation. A form is an excellent first opportunity to record evidence and facts about an accident. A basic accident form is illustrated in Exhibit 12.3. Companies can develop customized forms to ensure consistency of their accident investigations.

Accident Reports

Accident reports should be written for major accidents, injuries, fatalities, property damage, and even near misses with potential for major injury or damage. A report should include a description of the accident sequence, the facts and analysis, causal factors, and corrective actions. This professional document will be used not only for

Exhibit 12.3

ACCIDENT FORM	
NAME	OCCUPATION
DATE	TIME
NATURE OF INJURY	BODY PART INJURED
LOCATION	

TASK AT TIME OF INJURY

ACCIDENT DESCRIPTION

CAUSAL FACTORS

CORRECTIVE ACTIONS

PREPARED BY	DATE

documentation, but also to prevent future accidents by initiating the corrective actions listed.

Accident reports should, at a minimum, contain:

- **Introduction.** Discusses the purpose of the investigation and brief background of the facility and accident.

- **Methodology.** Discusses the accident investigation and the techniques used to determine the sequence of events, causal factors, and corrective actions.

- **Sequence of events (a thorough accident description).** This is a chronological sequence of the accident events. A portion of the events and causal factors chart may be included.

- **Facts and analysis.** Results of analytical techniques, possibly divided into topic areas. This part should flow logically into the next two parts.

- **Causal factors.**

- **Corrective actions.**

- **Conclusions and summary.** A summary of the investigation and its outcomes (Vincoli 1994) (DOE 1999).

Report-Writing Tips

- Be objective. State the facts of the accident and assign causes and causal relationships. Do not assign blame.

- Write in a style that everyone can follow, not like you are describing a technical procedure.

- Do not include people's names in the report; they are not important at this level of documentation. Job titles could be used instead of names.

- Break the facts into topic areas such as training, management oversight, electrical safety, explosives, or machine maintenance. For the example scenario, the topic areas could be forklift activities, management (supervision), communication, and possibly ladder safety. The facts in these topic areas are listed and analyzed. If there are multiple topic areas, the responsibility for reporting on them can be assigned to different people.

- Insert graphics and tables into the report to convey the information more effectively.
- Link causal factors to corrective actions with a simple table.

Accident Trending

One of the latest advancements in the accident investigation process is accident trending. Trending is the process of using a database to analyze accident trends and find out what areas, jobs, tasks, or programs are having the most accidents and why. For example, the discovery that one department is responsible for more medical calls than another may be an indicator that a major accident could occur in that department. If trending information such as this is used to make changes to reduce accidents, it is called proactive trending. Accident and medical logs are excellent sources for trending data. The more information received about an accident, the more trending opportunities there will be.

Many companies use trending to create colorful graphs and charts without actually focusing on problem areas and correcting the problems. It is important to remember that accident trending will not prevent accidents unless corrective actions are taken. If a trend is found—such as that electricians seem to be receiving three times as many shocks this year as last—the reasons (perhaps tool or procedure changes) must be determined and corrective actions taken.

Another problem with trending is that it may oversimplify accident analysis because, to keep things simple and make pretty charts, companies may choose to follow only a few root causes and base all of their trending on these causes. Unfortunately, this type of trending does not help to prevent problems. The root causes chosen by the companies—human error, procedures not followed, management failure, supervision not adequate—are too broad to have useful corrective actions. For example, if a company finds that 60 percent of the causes of its accidents are "management failure," what will the corrective actions be? Give management more training? Training in what? The cause is too vague. If this happens, trending analysis will have lost its purpose.

Besides documenting information about types of accidents and which departments have the most accidents, trending and accident analysis can be used to show how many accidents occur on each day of the week or month; how many happen to each gender, age group, or department; how many happen at certain times of day or on certain shifts; how many happen to long-term versus short-term employees; how many happen to people doing a certain type of work or using a particular procedure; which causal factors are responsible for the most accidents; which corrective actions are most often recommended; even what position employees were standing or sitting in when an accident occurred and what body parts are most often injured. Trending is an important tool for preventing accidents and correcting weaknesses in the safety program.

Follow-up Steps

- **Check that the corrective action has been completed correctly.** If a corrective action database is used, make a notation in the database when the corrective action has been completed.

- **Make certain the corrective action works to prevent accidents.** A new procedure must be tested to ensure that the problem was corrected and accidents will be prevented.

- **Ensure that the corrective action is being used.** If a new procedure was written, you will know that the corrective action was completed; however, the more important issue is that the new procedure is actually being used.

- **Be proactive.** A follow-up is an excellent opportunity to observe hazards in the field. When performing the follow-up, check to see if any other hazards could cause an accident. Any hazard that has the potential to cause injury, illness, or damage should be analyzed and corrected. Also keep in mind that a corrective action could have been completed correctly, but the changes it caused to the system may have created additional hazards that must now be corrected. For example, requiring maintenance workers to wear extensive personal protective equipment may lead to heat-related illnesses in warm weather. The follow-up is the last line of defense in the accident investigation process. This step should ensure a safe and healthy workplace free of hazards.

Summary

Documentation is an important part of the accident investigation process. The three types of documentation used are accident logs, accident forms, and accident reports. All types of accident investigation documentation should convey the facts of the investigation, the causal factors of the accident, and the corrective actions that will prevent future accidents. Once accidents are logged into a computer database, trending can be used to prevent accidents and correct weaknesses in the safety program. The prevention of accidents is based on the initiation, completion, and use of corrective actions, and a follow-up ensures that these steps are performed. (Please see the Appendix for a sample Accident Investigation form.)

REVIEW QUESTIONS

1. What are the three types of accident investigation documentation?

2. What should be included in an accident investigation report?

3. What are some trending categories?

4. What is proactive trending?

5. What is a follow-up?

6. For the example accident scenario, prepare and document a full accident report that includes the introduction, methodology, accident sequence, facts, analysis, causal factors, and corrective actions, conclusions, and summary.

Appendix

Charts and forms to help you analyze accidents:

Analytical Tree Flowchart
Change Analysis Form
Barrier Analysis Form
Accident Investigation Form

You may photocopy or remove these pages.

ANALYTICAL TREE FLOWCHART

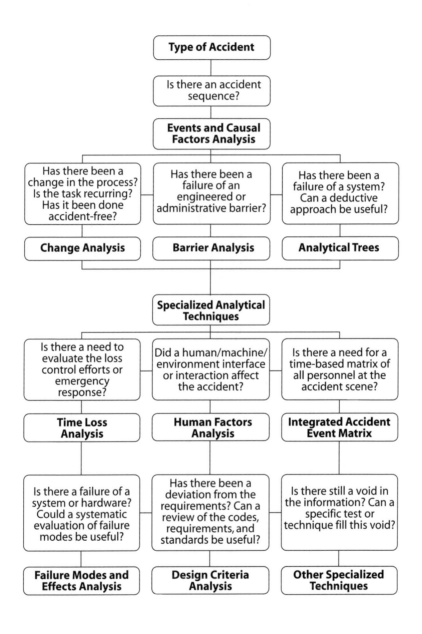

CHANGE ANALYSIS FORM

ACCIDENT SEQUENCE	COMPARISON SEQUENCE	DIFFERENCE	ANALYSIS

BARRIER ANALYSIS FORM

BARRIER	PURPOSE OF BARRIER	PERFORMANCE OF BARRIER

ACCIDENT INVESTIGATION FORM

NAME	OCCUPATION
DATE	TIME
NATURE OF INJURY	BODY PART INJURED
LOCATION	
TASK AT TIME OF INJURY	
ACCIDENT DESCRIPTION	
CAUSAL FACTORS	
CORRECTIVE ACTIONS	
PREPARED BY	DATE

Glossary

Accident – The occurrence in a sequence of events that produced unintended injury, death, or property damage.

Accident form – A form used to collect information about an accident, document the accident, and list causal factors and corrective actions.

Accident investigation – A structured process that uncovers the sequence of events that produced or had the potential to produce an accident and determines the accident's causal factors and corrective actions.

Accident investigator – A person responsible for investigating an accident.

Accident log – A list of an organization's accidents, injuries, and near misses.

Accident Ratio Study – A study made in the 1960s that found that for every major injury that occurs, ten minor injuries, thirty property damage incidents, and six hundred near misses occur.

Accident theories – Points of view about how and why accidents occur.

Accountability levels – An organization's areas of responsibility, ranging from responsibility for setting company philosophy to performing physical tasks. See *corporate level, management level, supervisor level, equipment level,* and *worker level.*

Administrative barriers – Processes and procedures that are intended to prevent accidents, such as approved work methods, job training, and supervisory control.

Analysis – A systematic and exhaustive thought process to find what is unknown.

Analytical – Describes the systematic thought process of breaking down information.

Analytical techniques – Investigative methods that help an accident investigator to systematically break down information.

Analytical tree – A graphical display of information that helps an accident investigator to deductively analyze a system in order to determine paths to failure or success.

Barrier – Something that keeps a hazard from coming into contact with workers. Barriers can be "hard" (engineered) or "soft" (administrative).

Barrier analysis – Identification and study of barriers associated with an accident.

Catastrophic accident – An accident involving a fatality, multiple injuries, or major property damage.

Causal analysis – The process of probing, discovering, and using scenarios, facts, tests, and assumptions to determine what caused an accident.

Causal factors – One or more events or circumstances that helped to produce an accident. A causal factor answers the question "What happened to cause this accident?"

Causes – Events that lead to injury, property damage, or illness.

Change analysis – Comparing a process that led to an accident with the process as it is usually performed, as it should have been performed according to company standards, or as it would ideally be performed .

Condition – Situation related to the event, such as "What caused that event to happen?" or "Why did that event happen?" Used with Events and Causal Factors charts.

Corporate level – The highest level of accountability in an organization. The organization's culture, philosophy, and style are defined at this level.

Corrective action – An action taken to prevent recurrence of an accident.

Deductive approach – An analytical technique that goes from general to specific.

Design criteria analysis – A technique that identifies standards that should be followed in performing a task and describes how to accomplish the task while complying with these standards.

Domino theory – An accident causation theory that compares the steps leading to an accident and the accident itself to a row of dominos that collapses when one is pushed.

Engineered barrier – A physical mechanism that prevents accidents. Examples: machine guards, protective equipment.

Equipment level – Along with the worker level, the lowest level of accountability for an accident.

Event – An occurrence in an accident sequence described by using a subject and verb and assigned a time and date.

Events and causal factors analysis – A technique that determines an accident sequence and analyzes the sequence to find why the accident happened.

Evidence – Anything that can be used to gain knowledge about an accident's sequence and its causes.

Failure modes and effects analysis – A technique for studying failures and how failures affect a system.

Failure – A mishap or unintentional occurrence in personnel, equipment, or environment.

Fault tree analysis – A graphical technique that may be used qualitatively to determine failures or faults in a system or quantitatively to determine failure rates.

First–aid case – An accident involving a minor injury.

Follow–up – The process of ensuring that corrective actions recommended during an accident investigation are initiated, completed, and used.

Hazard – A situation or equipment with the potential to cause injury.

Hazard control precedence – A hazard reduction strategy that lists changes in order of their effectiveness in preventing accidents.

Human factors analysis – A technique for identifying human/ machine/environment interfaces or interactions.

Integrated accident event matrix – A technique in which the investigator makes a chart of all individuals at the scene of an accident and their actions during the time immediately preceding the accident.

Interview – The process of gathering information from an individual by asking questions.

Management level – The level of accountability that dictates an organization's policies and procedures.

Management Oversight and Risk Tree (MORT) – A systematic approach to analyzing the adequacy of programs, procedures, controls, and management systems.

Multiple causation theory – The hypothesis that accidents have multiple causes; they do not result from a single cause.

Near miss – An occurrence in a sequence of events that had the potential to produce an accident.

OSHA 300 log – A list of an organization's recordable injuries and illnesses as prescribed by the OSHA Recordkeeping Standard.

Paper evidence – Written documentation related to an accident.

People evidence – Evidence gathered from people, usually in the form of statements and interviews.

Photograph evidence – Photographs or videotapes that document an accident scene.

Physical evidence – Hardware and solid material related to an accident.

Property damage accident – An incident involving damage to property or equipment.

Recommendations – Actions proposed to prevent recurrence of an accident. Also called *corrective actions*.

Recordable injury – Injury or illness deemed recordable under OSHA Recordkeeping Standard.

Report – Written documentation of an accident that conveys the facts of the investigation, causal factors of the accident, and recommended corrective actions.

Root cause – The ultimate cause of an accident. For the purposes of this book it is called a *causal factor*.

Root cause analysis – A technique for determining the ultimate cause of an accident.

Safety program – Policies and procedures developed by an organization to prevent accidents and illnesses.

Sequence of events – The order in which events leading up to an accident occurred.

Supervisor level – This level of accountability dictates how work is to be done.

Trending – Using a computerized database to analyze accident patterns.

Time loss analysis – A technique for evaluating how the timing of emergency responses or loss control actions affected the loss caused by an accident and analyzing the losses that occurred as the accident progressed.

Witness statement – A description of an accident written by someone associated with the accident.

Worker level – This is the lowest level of accountability, where the work is performed and the equipment is operated.

Bibliography

ABS Consulting, Inc. "RootCause LEADER 2.0." June 2003. http://www.abs-jbfa.com/rootcauseleader.html.

Adams, E. "The Quality Revolution: A Challenge to Safety Professionals." *Professional Safety,* August 1991: 22-28.

Apollo Associated Services. "RealityCharting™." June 2003. http://www.apollo-as.com/rc/cont.htm.

Bahr, Nicholas. *System Safety Engineering and Risk Assessment: A Practical Approach.* Greenbelt, MD: Hernandez Engineering, Inc., 1997.

Benner, Ludwig. "Accident Investigation: Multilinear Events Sequencing Methods." *Journal of Safety Research,* June 1975: 67-73.

Bird E. Frank and Germain L. George. *Practical Loss Control Leadership.* Loganville, GA: International Loss Control Institute, 1985.

Bird, E. Frank and Harold E. O'Shell. "Incident Recall." *National Safety News,* October 1969.

Crowl, Daniel A. and Louvar, Joseph F. *Chemical Process Safety: Fundamentals with Applications.* Englewood, NJ: Simon and Schuster Co., 1990.

Decision Systems, Inc. "REASON® 5 Root Cause Analysis Software." June 2003. http://www.rootcause.com/REASON4.htm.

Department of Energy. *Conducting Accident Investigations.* Rev. 2, DOE, 1999.

Ferry, Ted S. *Elements of Accident Investigation,* Springfield, IL: Charles C. Thomas, 1978.

————. *Modern Accident Investigation and Analysis.* (New York: John Wiley and Sons, 1981.

Geller, Scott. "The Myth of the Root Cause." *ISHN,* June 2002: 18-20.

Gibson, J. J. *Behavioral Approaches to Accident Research.* New York: Association for the Aid of Crippled Children, 1961.

Haddon, W. "On the Escape of Tigers: An Ecological Note." *Technical Review,* 1970, 72:44.

————. "A Logical Framework for Categorizing Highway Safety Phenomena and Activity." *Journal of Trauma,* 12 1972: 197.

Hammer, Willie. *Product Safety Management and Engineering,* 2nd ed. Des Plaines, IL: American Society of Safety Engineers, 1993.

Handley, C. "Quality Improvement Through Root Cause Analysis." *Hospital Material Management Quarterly,* May 2000: 74-78.

Heinrich, H. W. *Industrial Accident Prevention.* New York: McGraw-Hill Book Co., 1936.

————. *Industrial Accident Prevention,* 4th edition. New York: McGraw-Hill Book Co., 1959.

Johnson, William G. *MORT: The Management Oversight and Risk Tree.* Washington, DC: Government Printing Office, 1973.

Kletz, Trevor. *Learning from Accidents in Industry.* Boston: Butterworth-Heinemann, 1988.

Marshall, Gilbert. *Safety Engineering,* 3rd ed. Des Plaines, IL: American Society of Safety Engineers, 2000.

Metzgar, Carl R. "The Changing Approach to the Epidemiology, Prevention, and Amelioration of Trauma." *Professional Safety,* April 2003: 17, 49.

National Safety Council. *Injury Facts.* Itasca, IL: National Safety Council, 2003.

————. *Accident Prevention Manual for Business and Industry,* 12th ed. Itasca, IL: National Safety Council, 2001

Oakley, Jeffrey and Smith, Susan. "Ergonomic Assessment and Design: The Key to Major Reduction in Back Injury." *Professional Safety,* February 2000: 35-38.

OSHA Institute. "Advanced Accident Investigation Course Workbook." January 10-13, 1995.

Peterson, Dan. *Techniques of Safety Management.* New York: McGraw-Hill Book Co., 1978.

Robertson, Leon S. *Injury Epidemiology,* 2nd ed. New York: Oxford University Press, 1998.

Senecal, Patricia and Burke, Ellen. "Root Cause Analysis: What Took Us So Long." *Occupational Hazards,* March 1994: 63-65.

Sorrell, Larry W. "Accident Investigation: Back to Reality." *Occupational Hazards,* September 1998: 39-40.

Spear, Jerome E. "Incident Investigation: A Problem Solving Process." *Professional Safety,* April 2002: 25-30.

Speir, Richard O. "Punishment in Accident Investigation." *Professional Safety,* August 1998: 29-31.

Stephenson, Joe. *System Safety 2000.* New York: Van Nostrand Reinhold, 1991.

System Improvements, Inc. "TapRooT® Software." June 2003. http://www.taproot.com/pages/software.htm.

System Safety Development Center. *Barrier Analysis.* DOE SSDC-29, 1985.

———. *Change Control and Analysis.* DOE SSDC-21, 1981.

———. *Guide to the Use of Change Analysis in Accident Investigation.* DOE SSDC-105, 1994.

———. *MORT Based Root Cause Analysis.* DOE SSDC-27, 1989.

———. *MORT User's Guide.* DOE SSDC-4, 1992.

———. *Time/Loss Analysis.* DOE SSDC-37, 1987.

System Safety Society. *Systems Safety Analysis Handbook,* 2nd ed. Albuquerque, NM: System Safety Society, 1997.

US Department of Health and Human Services. *Worker Health Chartbook 2000.* Cincinnati, OH: NIOSH, 2000.

U.S. Department of Labor. *Bloodborne Pathogens.* OSHA 1910.1030. 2003.

Vincoli, W. Jeffery. *A Basic Guide To Accident Investigation and Loss Control.* New York: John Wiley & Sons, 1994.

Bibliography

Index